FOOD PHARMACOLOGY

Publication Number 732

AMERICAN LECTURE SERIES ®

A Monograph in

The BANNERSTONE DIVISION of
AMERICAN LECTURES IN LIVING CHEMISTRY

Edited by

I. NEWTON KUGELMASS, M.D., Ph.D., Sc.D.
Consultant to the Departments of Health and Hospitals
New York, New York

FOOD

PHARMACOLOGY

———————————————— *By* ————————————————

N. SAPEIKA, B.A., M.D., Ph.D., F.R.S.S.Af.

Professor of Pharmacology
University of Cape Town
Cape Town, South Africa

CHARLES C THOMAS • PUBLISHER
Springfield • Illinois • U.S.A.

Published and Distributed Throughout the World by

CHARLES C THOMAS ● PUBLISHER

BANNERSTONE HOUSE

301-327 East Lawrence Avenue, Springfield, Illinois, U.S.A.

NATCHEZ PLANTATION HOUSE

735 North Atlantic Boulevard, Fort Lauderdale, Florida, U.S.A.

1969, by CHARLES C THOMAS ● PUBLISHER

Library of Congress Catalog Number: 68-25978

With THOMAS BOOKS *careful attention is given to all details of manufacturing and design. It is the Publisher's desire to present books that are satisfactory as to their physical qualities and artistic possibilities and appropriate for their particular use.* THOMAS BOOKS *will be true to those laws of quality that assure a good name and good will.*

Printed in the United States of America

E-1

To Simone,

Raphael, Karin, David

CONTENTS

Page

Foreword vii

Preface xi

Chapter

1. GENERAL CONSIDERATIONS 3
2. FOODS OF PLANT ORIGIN 16
3. FOODS OF ANIMAL ORIGIN 84
4. FOOD OF MARINE ANIMAL ORIGIN 99
5. FOOD ADDITIVES 108
6. FOOD CONTAMINANTS 127
7. WATER, SOFT DRINKS, AND ALCOHOLIC BEVERAGES . . . 135
   Bibliography 149
   Author Index 169
   Subject Index 174

5245

FOREWORD

Our Living Chemistry Series was conceived by Editor and Publisher to advance the newer knowledge of chemical medicine in the cause of clinical practice. The interdependence of chemistry and medicine is so great that physicians are turning to chemistry, and chemists to medicine in order to understand the underlying basis of life processes in health and disease. Only chemical truths, proofs and convictions become sound foundations for clinical phenomena, key hybrid investigators clarify the bewildering panorama of biochemical progress for application in everyday practice, stimulation of experimental research, and extension of postgraduate instructions. Each of our monographs thus unravels the chemical mechanisms and clinical management of many diseases that have remained relatively static in the minds of medical men for three thousand years. Our new Series is charged with the *nisus élan* of chemical wisdom, supreme in choice of international authors, optimal in standards of chemical scholarship, provocative in imagination for experimental research, comprehensive in discussions of scientific medicine, and authoritative in chemical perspective of human disorders.

Dr. Sapeika of Cape Town presents the chemical and biological hazards in "good" food. Every meal contains deliberate or accidental additions of dozens of possibly injurious non-nutritive compounds as chemical additives, condiments, toxicants, bioactive and pharmaco-active compounds in foods obtained from plants and land and marine animals and harmful synthetic substances in water, soft drinks and alcoholic beverages. Food micro-organisms present hazards from dangerous anaerobes. At first sight it may seem that sterile foods would eliminate microbial spoilage and food-borne disease. But it is not yet possible to process and market staple foods in a sterile state without losing enzymatic and nutritive values, and we must learn to live on in-fected foods with a bacterial count below 10^4 per gram. Bacterial inhibitors are added with safe consumer limits as preservatives and antibiotics. Salmonellae are destroyed by heat, irradiation and fumigation during production or before distribution. Parasites develop life cycles in animals and plants that serve as food for their definite hosts and remain hazards despite health education, im-proved sanitation and processed meat control.

Food additives are of ancient origin. Bread was baked with spices and condiments in 3000 B.C. Fish was salted and pickled in brine in 2300 B.C. Porridge was enlivened with fennel, mint, and safflower seeds in 1400 B.C. Food was seasoned with onions, garlic, pepper and anise in 1200 B.C. Early human society was transformed by the discovery of fire which enabled food preserva-tion by smoking that retained toxic smoke components such as pyroligenous acid, formaldehyde and potential carcinogens. The invention of agriculture introduced new poisons such as dead fish for fertilization, ethylene gas for ripening, sulfur dust for fungi-cides, but the primitive achievements opened new paths of pro-gress in herbicides, rodenticides, insecticides, defoliants, desiccants, fumigants, nematocides, disinfectants, sterilization.

Food preparation has changed from home production to mass production with additives to influence the desirability and edi-bility of food products, for one eats with one's eyes. In the past, the principal role of added substances was preservative as bacterio-static agents or deterioration inhibitors. At present, the role of additives is pacing with progress in food technology to include nu-trients, coloring and flavoring agents, neutralizers, humectants, coating agents, plasticizers, pesticides, plant growth regulators, androgens and estrogens. Chlorinated hydro-cooling reduces loss of fresh fruit during shipment. Growth-promoting hormones improve the quality of meat products. Hormone sprays prevent immature fruit from dropping in the vineyard. Antibiotics in food accelerate animal growth. Stabilizing agents prevent crystallization of frozen desserts. Curing and bleaching agents enhance baked products. Emulsifiers maintain the palatability of salad dressings. Calcium salts increase the firmness and stability of fruits. Silicones give antifoam action to fermentable foods. There are no harmless substances but only harmless ways of using substances. Noxious components causing goiter appear naturally in milk from cows fed excessive cabbage. Accidental contamination with excessive metal catalysts added to beer causes heart disease. Deliberate additions of some artificial colors in flour induces hemolytic anemia. Residues of pest and weed killers in eggs, milk and vegetables cause chemical poisoning. Food poison tastes good and so there is no protest.

Radioactivity in foods comes from fallout following testing of nuclear weapons with fission products in fish from marine disposal and milk from Sr^{90} consumption in fodder. Strontium and barium isotopes follow calcium for preferential deposition in bone. Periodic examination of radioactivity in foods, especially milk, is necessary to determine the degree of future hazard. New approaches to the evaluation of safety of raw materials and additives must be developed as we progress from simple processed food to more complex convenient products, and finally to foods based on isolated, purified and modified nutrients. The increasing world population calls for foods constructed from nutrients derived from non-foods with proper chemical and biological evaluations to assure absence of consumer hazard and preservation of nutritive values. Somehow, there are too few scientists concerned with the ways and means of assuring safe foods; too many problems associated with enforcement of laws and regulations for safe foods; too little standardization of laboratory tests for food inspection.

Physicians must be continually alert to the extent to which chemicals are found in food, to the symptoms of diseases that might be
induced, and to the methods of testing and control in the prevention of unsuspected poisoning. The Food and Drug Administration regulates foods moving in interstate commerce, but state
and local communities need laws for the safety of the consumer not
only in chemical but in biological hazards. Food problems are
often the same but food safety differs with each human era.

> *Eye hath not seen, nor ear heard,*
> *Neither hath it entered into*
> *the imagination of man,*
> *What findings are in store*
> *for them who diligently seek.*

I. Newton Kugelmass, M.D., Ph.D., Sc.D., *Editor*

PREFACE

The invitation to write this book has brought to the author the opportunity to assemble much information on pharmaco-active substances present in food and drink. A large and heterogeneous variety of such substances has been described in greater and lesser detail throughout the extensive medical and non-medical literature. Some of the chemical agents considered are always present in food as inherent genetically determined characteristics of the plant or animal used as food; some are present because of contamination from various environmental sources; some are there because of intentional or unintentional activities of man. Only a brief account is given of the pharmacological substances that may be present in the diet of man and animal, but the inclusion of numerous references will enable the interested reader to obtain more detailed information.

In order to make this volume as useful and comprehensive as possible, food and its pharmacology have been considered in the widest sense. Therefore an account is given of a large variety of substances of all kinds ingested by people and animals all over the world. Many of these "foods" are regularly used with little or no obvious effect produced by the ingredients which they contain. Some may only occasionally or unexpectedly produce disturbances in health and even death. A few are always harmful and are generally avoided, but they cause discomfort, disease and death, when eaten by persons ignorant of the dangers or when man or animal is driven by famine conditions to eat them.

N.S.

FOOD PHARMACOLOGY

Chapter 1

GENERAL CONSIDERATIONS

A food is defined as a substance that is taken to replace physiological waste of tissue, to supply energy and heat, and to build up tissues.

Food or nutriment is also the term generally used to indicate a mixture of foodstuffs which appeals to taste and satisfies hunger. The term foodstuff is applied to anything that can be used as food. It is in this wider sense that all food materials making up a diet, including condiments and beverages, have been considered in this book.

Active substances of natural origin and ingredients or contaminants of many different kinds introduced by man occur in a large variety of foods. Many of them are generally not significant, but there are a few that may on occasion seriously affect a single individual, groups of individuals, and sometimes hundreds and even thousands of animals or human beings, as for example in the case of poisoning with deadly mushrooms, mycotoxins such as aflatoxins, tri-orthocresyl phosphate, and pesticides. Even long-established foods may reveal unexpected dangers, as illustrated by the phenomenon in which a previously harmless and indeed nutritious food, namely cheese, has now become dangerous when the consumer is receiving treatment with antidepressant drugs such as the mono-amine oxidase inhibitors.

Much remains to be learned about many of the pharmacologically active substances that are naturally present in food or that may intentionally or accidentally come to be present in food. It

3

has been known to mankind for many years that there are natural products which are acutely toxic, but it is only relatively recently that it has been recognized that chronic effects may follow the ingestion of certain materials which do not necessarily produce acute effects. Also, there is scanty information about the possible adverse effects produced by the ingestion of mixtures or combination of foods.

BACTERIAL FOOD POISONING

This term covers a wide variety of illnesses. There are specific bacteria well known as causes of food poisoning, for example the *Salmonella* and *Shigella* organisms which multiply within the intestinal tract; such infections are not considered in this book. Certain bacteria synthesize specific toxic substances known as exotoxins and endotoxins; true food poisoning implies the ingestion of food in which exotoxin is already present. The bacterial species best known as causes of food poisoning in this context are *Clostridium botulinum* (botulism), *Staphylococcus aureus, Clostridium perfringens, Bacillus cereus, Vibro parahaemolyticus* and some other microorganisms. This type of food poisoning caused by the ingestion of preformed bacterial toxins has been considered by Thatcher (1966) in relation to comparative symptoms, procedures for extraction and purification of the causal toxins, their chemistry, serology, assay procedures and pharmacology, to the extent that these are known.

FOOD ALLERGY

This disorder occurs in some persons, i.e. they react abnormally under certain conditions to specific foodstuffs that do not affect the vast majority of people; for example there is the well-recognized sensitivity of some persons to strawberries, shellfish, milk, or eggs. The manifestations may include abdominal symptoms, also skin rashes; but almost all including the most unusual allergic manifestations can be evoked by foods. Consideration of foods that have been reported to act as allergens is presented by Urbach and Gottlieb (1946), Strauss (1964) and Mansmann

(1966). Gluten-sensitivity enteropathy may be regarded as an example of a specific sensitivity.

Individuals may occasionally show hypersensitivity to drugs present in food, as for example in the case of cow's milk containing penicillin. It is possible that attacks of migraine may be produced in certain susceptible individuals by tyramine and other amines present in certain foods such as cheese, fish, beans, milk dairy products, chocolate, and in alcoholic beverages (Hannington, 1967).

In asthmatic children the smell of fish can often induce violent allergic attacks, as reported by Aas (1966). Examples of allergy to the smell of food, for example garlic, onions, coffee and after cooking of peas, beans and lentils, are given by Urbach and Gottlieb (1946). While there is evidence that food components can act as antigens and allergens, there is a need for more investigation regarding the antigenicity and allergenicity of bacterial products and of additives and contaminants in food.

Certain artificial food colors are known to have caused urticaria in children who had eaten colored candies (sweets). Severe asthma has rarely occurred from tartrazine and certain other dyes commonly used to color drug tablets and capsules as well as many foods.

BIOACTIVE SUBSTANCES

Foods may cause untoward effects or poisoning because of their content of "naturally-occurring" pharmaco-active substances as for example in the case of ergot, favus beans, mushrooms, rhubarb, shellfish, snakeroot and because of the presence of contaminating poisons such as aflatoxins in groundnut meal and *Senecio* alkaloids in bread. A review of many foods and the substances they elaborate as natural constituents or which they derive from contaminating sources is given in detail in later chapters of this book.

FOOD ADDITIVES AND FOOD CONTAMINANTS

Food may be harmful because of additives or contaminants introduced by man. Food additives are foreign non-nutritive substances intentionally added to enhance the taste, the structure, or the storage life of food. Food contaminants include harmful man-made foreign substances such as pesticides and radionuclides that have accidentally become included in food.

Food additives have been introduced into all kinds of foods by food technologists. The requirements of our developed society have necessitated that the foods we eat are in many instances prepared and preserved by the addition of chemical substances which are regarded as harmless. There is no reason to believe that the chemicals added to foods by manufacturers of foods are endangering health. They are either intrinsically nontoxic or not harmful in the concentrations permitted by law. In certain countries there are special organizations, for example in the United States of America the Food and Drug Administration, which serve to protect consumers from hazardous chemicals. In the United States also there is the Food, Drug and Cosmetic Act of 1938, with subsequent amendments which provide for tolerances of pesticides used on raw agricultural products, and the testing and approval of the safety of new food additives and color additives. In England there is an official Food Additives and Contaminants Committee.

Some additives have long been used and are generally regarded as safe, but these as well as newer chemicals used in foods need thorough evaluation, regarding their safety, through modern scientific methods of investigation. It is not possible to be completely certain that these additives will never produce harmful effects in the same way as it is never possible to say with nearly 100 per cent certainty that a particular drug has no untoward effects. Nevertheless the use of chemicals has become a necessary part of modern food production and processing. The world is short of food, and the shortage grows worse as the population increases. Substances which prolong the shelf life of food or which diminish wastage are very important.

The problem of food safety is of growing complexity and diversity and much research is needed to provide practical methods for preventing, detecting and removing non-nutritive constituents of food that may be harmful. This is apart from the continuing need for investigating the effects of long-term exposure to small amounts of food-borne pharmacological and toxic agents, and with due regard to the difficulty of extrapolating the results obtained in laboratory experiments on animals to those potentially possible in man. It is not the substances that produce severely acute toxic effects but rather those which have a slow or cumulative effect that are probably of greatest practical importance. It seems possible that with increasing recognition and knowledge of chemicals consumed by man and animal that the causes of some previously mysterious diseases may be revealed.

Many different chemicals used as additives in foods have not been adequately tested for carcinogenic or other harmful properties. Obviously those that cause malignant or other serious changes in animals of one species or another should be forbidden for human consumption. It cannot be sufficiently emphasized that tests in animals are of limited value, because relatively big doses of chemicals may be administered to them to obtain results in the shortest possible time; different species may react in different ways; the route of administration and other technical aspects may determine the result; the positive or negative results observed are not necessarily transferable to man. Potential or actual carcinogens in foods may be regarded as weak in action, but the cumulative effects may cause cancer to develop in a relatively large percentage of the total population at risk. Much attention through research and testing is being directed to the role of food additives and other food constituents as actual, potential or synergistic factors in the genesis of neoplasms (Hueper, 1961; Kraybill, 1963). Experts who have considered carcinogenic hazards and other possible ill effects which might arise from food additives are agreed on the principle that only substances which are considered to be innocuous should be permitted. This is safer than the older system in which only substances known to be harmful were banned.

Many chemicals have come to be used as food additives, and experts in food technology must draw up standards for their control. Preferably there should be international agreement on such standards, but this exists in relatively few instances. Most countries in the world have agreed to work to permitted lists, with guidance from the World Health Organization and Food and Agricultural Organization of the United Nations, although national sovereignty is still retained (Kekwick, 1965).

In addition to food additives, food contamination also is considered in more detail in a later section of this book, but some general introductory remarks are included here. Antibiotics may come to be present in foods in a number of different ways, for example when used as preservatives for certain foods, or as a result of their administration in the prophylaxis and treatment of infections in animals used as food. The treatment of bovine mastitis with penicillin has created risks to human health because of the presence of penicillin excreted in the cow's milk.

There has been some concern about the storage of pesticides, especially the chlorinated hydrocarbon insecticides such as DDT, in the fat of mammals. Residues of this persistent insecticide have been found, sometimes hundreds of miles from the nearest spraying operation, in the bodies of animals throughout the world, including birds from the Arctic and Antarctic regions. In view of the dangers, a WHO Expert Committee in 1962 published a report on principles governing consumer safety in relation to pesticide residues.

Pesticide residues have now accumulated to levels that are catastrophic for certain animal populations especially carnivorous birds (Woodwell, 1967). Organic chlorine residues have been found in fish and birds from the Atlantic and Pacific Oceans, and in marine crustacea and mollusca (Robinson *et al.*, 1967). The eggs of different species of sea-birds taken from sites around the British coast have been shown to contain such residues which had presumably been derived from insecticides in their fish diet. The contamination of cow's milk and human milk and of hens' eggs with pesticides, especially with organo-chlorine residues, is referred to in relevant sections of this book.

The problem of possible potentiation and additive effects of pesticides in the daily diet and of potentiation of pesticides by drugs such as the phenothiazines is considered by Fitzhugh (1966). Potentiating effects have been observed in both man and animals, but more information is required before the extrapolation of data from animal experiments to humans and the establishment of safe tolerance levels can be clearly indicated.

Food contamination has recently come to the fore in connection with the recognition of the production of aflatoxins and other toxins by molds such as *Aspergillus* growing in groundnut meal and other food material (Symposium on Mycotoxicosis, 1965; de Wit *et al.*, 1966; Feuell, 1966; Wogan, 1966; Purchase, 1967; Schoental, 1967). The possibility of this type of carcinogen, and other fungal toxins (Wilson, 1966), being toxic to man has caused concern about the use of certain foods, for example the use of peanut meal as a milk substitute and an economical food in certain countries. The relationship of foods, feeds, food additives and food degradation products to carcinogenesis has been much discussed in recent years (Petering, 1966; Miller, 1966). There are many examples of potential carcinogens for man and animals. These include the carcinogen responsible for hepatoma in rainbow trout, the hepatocarcinogenic aflatoxins present in fungus-contaminated grain and peanuts and in the milk of cows given such contaminated food, the carcinogens luteoskyrin and islanditoxin which are present as a common contaminant of rice and rice products used by Asiatic peoples, and the very potent carcinogen cycasin present as a natural ingredient, not as a contaminant, in unrefined cycad meal (Roe and Lancaster, 1964).

The possible significance of *N*-nitrosamines as causal factors in human carcinogenesis is based on the widespread occurrence of nitrosamine precursors in biological systems and the remarkable way in which various nitrosamines can affect different organs in the same species of experimental animal (Bonser, 1967). This is important in the current search for nitrosamines or other agents in the environment which may induce esophageal and other cancers in man (see Mushrooms; Bantu beer).

There are other examples of potentially carcinogenic food and feed used in many parts of the world; this includes cow's milk as a source of carcinogens. Such foods and feeds are being intensively examined as likely causes of the high incidence of cancer. Liver and stomach cancer are very prevalent in many parts of the world and these particularly are being investigated.

The presence of radionuclides in foods has been and is being demonstrated and the problem of safety levels regularly studied in many countries. Everyone is now exposed not only to natural radiation but to some additional radiation such as that from strontium-90. This radionuclide is with us to stay because of its long half-life of twenty eight years. The presence of such substances as contaminants in milk and other foods is considered in a later section.

ORDINARY FOODS HARMUL IN CERTAIN INDIVIDUALS

Foods that are well known and widely used without causing harmful effects may cause disturbances in certain individuals who have basic disorders that may be aggravated or precipitated by an offending food substance. The following are cited as examples; they include hypersensitivity (allergy) to certain foods and inborn errors of metabolism.

a. Allergic disorders such as urticaria, asthma and possibly migraine may result from the ingestion of certain foods by predisposed subjects. Penicillin in cow's milk is also a cause of hypersensitivity reactions.

b. Celiac disease is to be regarded as a gluten-induced enteropathy and the basis of treatment is, therefore, a gluten-free diet plus certain supplements (see Wheat). Gluten is a protein contained in wheat flour and rye flour, but not in pure wheat or rye starch.

c. In hepatic cirrhosis with liver failure, no protein should be given by mouth while the patient is receiving the special treatment for this complication; also other nitrogen-containing substances, for example ammonium chloride, should be excluded — otherwise hepatic encephalopathy is likely to be produced (see Meat).

d. Maple syrup urine disease, so called from the characteristic odor of the urine, is an inborn error of the metabolism of branched-chain amino acids; the withdrawal of valine, leucine, isoleucine and methionine from the diet has produced some benefit (Review, 1965).

e. Favism is a hemolytic disorder induced by the ingestion of the fava bean or by contact with the pollen of the plant; the red blood cells in these patients are deficient in the enzyme glucose-6-phosphate dehydrogenase (G-6 PD) which plays an important part in the metabolism of glucose and is necessary for the continued integrity of the cell. These red blood cells are also sensitive to a number of drugs, for example primaquine, sulphonamide and vitamin-K analogues. (Vitamin-K analogues can also be toxic by causing a hyperbilirubinemia when given to an infant or when given to mothers late in pregnancy.)

f. Phenylketonuria (phenylpyruvic oligophrenia) is a classical example of an inborn metabolic error of amino acid metabolism in which mental deficiency will occur unless a diet sufficiently low in phenylalanine content is started early (Review, 1961). Inhibition of vitamin B_6 contributes to the pathogenesis of this disease (Hoong Loo and Ritman, 1967).

Expert dietetic treatment is started on a phenylalanine-free food such as casein hydrolysate which has been freed of phenylalanine and to which have been added certain amino acids, fats, minerals, carbohydrates and vitamins. The treatment is very expensive and requires hospital supervision.

g. Galactosemia is a well-known, but rare, inborn error of metabolism in which the basic defect is enzymatic; the red cells are deficient in galactose 1 phosphate-uridyl-transferase. The body is unable to convert galactose to glucose. The manifestations of the disease include vomiting, jaundice, failure of growth, and later cirrhosis and lenticular cataracts appear (Review, 1962). These features may be prevented or reversed in many of the affected infants if the diagnosis is made early and a lactose-free diet given. The signs and symptoms regress after the elimination of milk and milk products from the diet (Hsia, 1967). Galactose is not present in fruits or vegetables.

h.   Porphyria may be produced in certain individuals by alcohol and by drugs such as barbiturates and other substances.

HYPERVITAMINOSIS

The importance of vitamins as essential food factors is well known.   They are ordinarily obtained as constituents of most foods; information on this subject is available in *Documenta Geigy-Scientific Tables* (1962) .   When taken in adequate amounts they prevent the development of deficiency diseases and help to maintain optimum health.   However, when pure potent vitamins especially those of the fat-soluble type are given in excess, they act as poisons.   Details are given by many authors including Locket (1957), Goodman and Gilman (1965), Ostwald and Briggs (1966) and by Meyler (1966); other references are given below.

Vitamin-A intoxication is recognized as two forms: (a) The acute type is due to the ingestion of a single large dose.   For example the livers of the polar bear and certain other animals are toxic in this way; they are extremely rich in vitamin A (see Liver).   Potent therapeutic vitamin-A preparations have caused serious poisoning when given to young infants and children (Review, 1964; 1965; Goodman and Gilman, 1965).   A single dose of the vitamin, 300,000 units, in young infants has produced bulging fontanelles from increased intracranial pressure, vomiting and other features.   (b) Chronic poisoning results from the daily ingestion of moderately toxic amounts over a considerable period of time, for example in the treatment of certain disorders. It produces impairment of skeletal development, hepatomegaly, splenomegaly, anemia, clubbing and coarse sparse hair.   The disorder may occur in food faddists (Bergen and Roels, 1965) .   Hypercarotenosis resuting from intake of large amounts of the provitamin-beta-carotene is innocuous (see Carrots).

Idiopathic hypercalcemia of children is similar to vitamin-A poisoning.   The disease probably has its origin in an alkaline diet combined with vitamin D and cow's milk, since the latter contains five times as much calcium and phosphorus as breast milk;

an idiopathic factor and hypersensitivity to the vitamin appear to be involved. Potent vitamin D preparations administered to children have caused loss of appetite, emaciation, diarrhea, and metastatic calcification.

Large and repeated doses of vitamin K analogues should not be given parenterally to newborn infants as serious disturbances including hyperbilirubinemia, jaundice and kernicterus have been produced (Review, 1961). Also, vitamin K taken by the mother late in pregnancy can adversely affect the fetus (Goodman and Gilman, 1965).

Nicotinic acid also when ingested in large amounts may produce pharmacological and harmful effects. An outbreak of food poisoning has occurred from the eating of adulterated meat in which nicotinic acid was an additive to prevent darkening of the meat; the symptoms included flushing and itching of the face and neck, sweating, nausea and abdominal cramps. In large doses given for prolonged periods this vitamin has produced hyperglycemia, jaundice and gastrointestinal symptoms including the development of peptic ulcer. Taken in large doses for months it can aggravate diabetes mellitus (Review, 1961; Molnar *et al.*, 1964).

HYPOVITAMINOSIS

This is of course well known. It occurs commonly and may be due to primary dietary deficiency in conditions of poverty or neglect, in mental defectives and in food faddists. Secondary vitamin deficiency usually results from disorders of the alimentary tract, but it may occur also during growth, pregnancy and lactation. There are certain drugs that can interfere with the biosynthesis of vitamins in the gut, and there are certain foods that contain antivitamins (Lepkovsky, 1966); some examples of antivitamins in foods are considered in later sections of this book.

CLASSIFICATION OF PHARMACO-ACTIVE FOODS

A satisfactory classification of foods from the point of view of pharmacology has presented difficulties. One arrangement that could be used is as follows: pharmaco-active substances always present in food but not harmful, for example bananas, pineapples; pharmaco-active substances always present and harmful, for example death-cup mushrooms, polar bear liver; pharmaco-active substances occasionally present and then harmful, for example paralytic shellfish toxin (saxitoxin); bread poisoning, drugs or poisons in milk.

Another classification that might be used would be based on the main organ or system affected by harmful substances, for example liver damage from *Senecio* alkaloids, aflatoxins and hepatotoxic mushrooms.

Classification might be made according to the source of the pharmaco-active principles. There are substances of fungal origin, for example aflatoxins, ergot alkaloids; of plant origin, for example *Senecio* alkaloids; of marine origin, for example shellfish toxin.

Pharmacologically active substances that may be present in food are considered in this book under the following headings:

Pharmaco-active substances in foods of plant origin

Pharmaco-active substances in foods of land animal origin

Pharmaco-active substances in foods of marine animal origin

Food additives and food contaminants of human technological origin

Water, fruit juices, soft drinks, tea and related beverages, alcoholic beverages

There have been numerous reports based on a tremendous amount of work and study on the subject of diet and coronary heart disease. A distinct association of coronary artery disease with high intake of fats and animal proteins has been demonstrated, although this is not claimed to be the only factor (Review, 1960). Dietary characteristics with special consideration of animal fats, sugar, alcohol and other substances, distribution of blood lipid levels, extent of atherosclerosis, and the frequency of coronary heart disease in various population groups have been described in much detail (Reviews, 1964, 1965, 1966). Some aspects of these studies are considered in this book.

A brief and simple review of the subject of the pharmacology of food has been published (Sapeika, 1965), and a well-documented monograph on toxicants occurring naturally in foods has recently been published (National Academy of Sciences, 1966) with contributions by a number of authors.

Chapter 2

FOODS OF PLANT ORIGIN

Many vegetable materials used routinely and traditionally as food contain potentially harmful substances, for example rhubarb and spinach contain oxalates, and one type of cassava plant from which tapioca is prepared contains cyanide. Many other examples are given in the following pages. The poisonous principle may be present only in small amount, or is eliminated by the traditional methods of selection and preparation of such plants for eating.

POISONOUS FRUITS

A number of plants are eaten by adults and by children as edible fruit or seeds, or they may be eaten in times of food shortage or famine. They may produce poisoning. A few examples are given below, and others are mentioned later in the text. For fuller details about the plants, the publication of Steyn (1949) and Watt and Breyer-Brandwyk (1962) may be consulted.

a.   The fresh or dried fruit pulp of several species of *Strychnos*, known by such names as Kaffir orange, wild orange, monkey orange, monkey apple, is eaten in southern Africa. *Strychnos punges Solered.* is usually edible but it may be toxic, causing vomiting, headache and giddiness; the seed is not eaten, as a large quantity may produce diarrhea. There are also other edible species. The fruit of certain species is stated to be highly toxic, for example *Strychnos stuhlmanii Gilg.* produces acute strychnine-like symptoms.

16

b. Certain *Adenia* species are eaten by stock and occasionally by man, but there is danger of poisoning from hydrocyanic acid. It is difficult to distinguish edible from poisonous species, as in the case of *Adenia hastata Schinz.* which resembles *Passiflora edulis Sims* (granadilla or passion fruit) and is edible. There is much scope for investigation in this field.

c. The fruit of various *Opuntia* (prickly pear) species is edible and is much eaten fresh, dried and in relishes, porridges and fermented drinks. When eaten in excess there is the danger of obstruction of the bowel being produced, and hematuria also has been reported. The leaf, from which the spines have been removed, has been used as a stock feed, for example in southern Texas and in South Africa. The nutritive value is low, but it provides water and it serves mechanically to remove parasites from the alimentary canal. The oxalate content may produce harmful effects.

d. Cultivated species of the *Cucurbitaceae* may be bitter and poisonous, for example marrows, gem squashes and watermelons; these may sometimes cause serious poisoning and death. The bitter principles are called cucurbitacins.

e. The fruit pulp of *Acanthosicyos horrida Welw.*, which is rich in protein, and the oil-containing seeds known in South Africa as butterpit, are eaten by the Hottentots and the Bushman near Walfish Bay in southwest Africa. The unripe fruit is intensely bitter.

f. The raw fruit pulp of *Ximenia americana L.* (hog plum, mountain plum, seaside plum, sour plum, wild plum, wild olive, yellow plum) is edible, and is used for dessert and jelly. The kernel is regarded as toxic, and some investigators have found cyanogens in the fruit and the leaf.

g. Several species of *Encephalartos* are edible. Some are known as broodboom or Kaffir bread because the stem contains starch that is used as meal or sago. The seed which has the shape and size of a date, and is known as wild date, has also been eaten after first being steeped in water to remove poison. The fruit is a characteristic cone and children have been known to eat the gum which exudes therefrom in certain species. However, the stem and the seed kernels of certain species are toxic; gastrointestinal symptoms are produced, and in animal experiments damage to the liver has been observed after the administration of the kernel.

Locusts or grasshoppers of various species are eaten by certain Bantu people, also by cattle, buffalo and sheep. Poisoning has occurred and sometimes death from poison which the insects themselves produce or which they have accumulated after feeding on some toxic substance present in plants such as *Nerium oleander* and *Asclepias fruiticosa* (Steyn, 1962). The black locust is poisonous from its content of the phytotoxin known as robin (Arena, 1963). Details of this toxic substance and the plant *Rominia pseudoacacia L.* from which it and other substances are derived are given by Watt and Breyer-Brandwyk (1962).

ACTIVE PRINCIPLES IN PLANTS

Poisonous plants in general are not considered in this volume, only such as have accidentally or deliberately been eaten as an adjunct or substitute for food. Such plants and their active principles are of many different kinds (Locket, 1957; Dewberry, 1959; Watt and Breyer-Brandwyk, 1962; Arena, 1963; Kingsbury, 1964).

Some active substances that are present in foods of plant origin are considered in the following paragraphs. Many others are reviewed later in connection with specific plants used as foods in various parts of the world.

Amines

It is well known that amines related to the aromatic amino acids occur in the animal body, and some are very potent, for example noradrenaline, adrenaline, 5-hydroxytryptamine (serotonin). These compounds and some others including dopamine and tyramine are present in certain fruits and vegetables used as human food, for example in bananas and plantains, tomatoes, avocado and pineapples. They are also found in certain cheeses especially cheddar, Camembert and Stilton, in certain wines, and in a number of other foods. The concentrations of various

amines in many foods are given by Udenfriend *et al.* (1959) **and**
Strong (1966) and other workers. Some of the values are shown
in the accompanying table. It is apparent that arylalkylamines
are more widespread in the plant kingdom than had been rea-
lized. The banana contains the largest amounts of these substances; the peel contains enormous quantities. Amounts are expressed as mg per 100 gm fresh fruit.

	Serotonin	*Tyramine*	*Dopamine*	*Noradrenaline*
Bananas (peel)	5-15	6.5	70	12.2
Bananas (pulp)	2.8	0.7	0.8	0.2
Plantain (pulp)	2-10	----	----	0.2
Pineapples (ripe)	2	----	----	----
Avocado	1	2.3	5	0
Tomato	1.2	0.4	0	0
Plum, red	1	0.6	0	+
Plum, blue	0	----	----	----
Eggplant	0.2	0.3	0	0
Potato	0	0.1	0	0.2
Orange	0	1.0	0	+

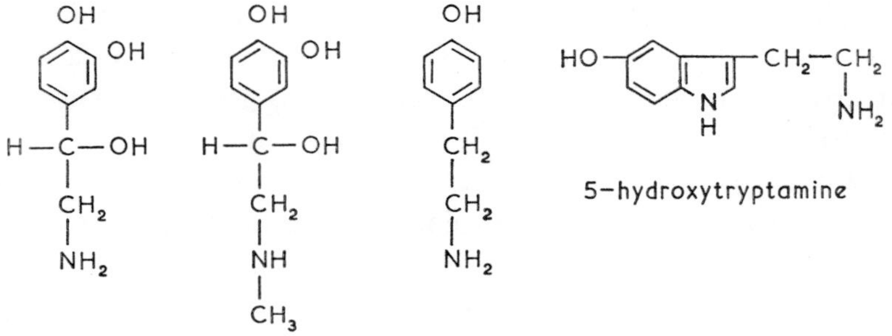

Noradrenaline

Adrenaline

Tyramine

5-hydroxytryptamine

The importance of these amines in relation to human health
is indicated in the sections of this book dealing with bananas,
cheese and alcohol.

Cyanogens

Many plant foodstuffs contain cyanogenetic glycosides together with one or more homologous enzymes, or they may contain cyanide in the form of nitrile. Cyanogens have been found
in maize, sorghum millet (Kaffir corn, American broom corn),
lima bean, kidney bean (haricot), sweet potato, manioc (cassava),

almond, linseed, bamboo shoots and certain other young shoots, and in many other plant materials such as the seeds of apples, apricots, cherries, pears, plums, prunes and other fruit. Bruising of these foodstuffs causes the interaction of enzyme and glycoside and the release of hydrocyanic acid. However, poisoning is rarely produced by most of these foodstuffs because the cyanogens such as the cyanogenetic glycosides are present in small amount, or in parts of the food (seeds, apple pips) which are not eaten. Poisoning has not infrequently occurred from the ingestion of manioc and lima beans; this is considered in more detail later in the individual sections dealing with these plant substances. The medical significance of the cyanogen in these foodstuffs has been considered by Montgomery (1965). The distribution and composition of cyanogenetic glycosides is considered by Liener (1966).

The seed of sorghum (*Sorghum dochna* Snowden), the common sorghum or great millet known in South Africa as Kaffir corn, which is used in the preparation of Bantu beer is edible but the plant is toxic to stock, the effects being due to the production of hydrocyanic acid from the cyanogenetic glycosides known as dhurrin. Details about this plant and related species and the factors involved in the production of hydrocyanic acid in plants under field conditions are given by Watt and Breyer-Brandwyk (1962).

In South Africa and certain other African countries many species of the genus *Acacia* are important as animal feed. The genus is an important source of tannin and gum (see Gums). Certain species are dangerous as they can produce hydrocyanic acid poisoning; they contain cyanogenetic glycosides.

The pod of *Acacia giraffae Willd.* (camelthorn, giraffe thorn, kameelboom, kameeldoring, mimosa) has been extensively used as feed for stock and is much relished by cattle. However, it has also produced poisoning and death from its content of hydrocyanic acid. The leaf of *Acacia lasiopetala Oliv.* is also a stock feed; it contains the cyanogenetic glycoside acacipetalin. Other acacia species also contain cyanogens (Watt and Breyer-Brandwyk, 1962).

Hepatotoxins

A number of plant and fungal poisons may contaminate animal feedstuffs or human food, and many of these will cause liver damage in animals and man. *Senecio* alkaloids, *Amanita* cyclopeptides, *Aspergillus* aflatoxins and other mycotoxins, and alcoholic beverages are among the important causes of pathological changes in the liver. These toxic agents are considered separately in relevant sections of this book (see also Review, 1964). It has become increasingly clear that the toxicity of molds must be considered in a wide variety of foodstuffs.

Metals

Normally vegetables and animal foods contain minute traces of many elements, and at times metals such as copper, arsenic, and iron are present but usually in small amounts. Selenium poisoning occurs in certain areas in the United States and other parts of the Americas, and in other countries, where fodder and grain are rich in selenium, due to the unusual amount of selenium in the soil (Frost, 1960). Farm animals in these areas suffer from poisoning; the disease has been known as alkali disease and blind staggers. Cattle are stunted in growth, emaciated, and in severe cases liver cirrhosis, anemia and death occur. Fowls that eat corn containing selenium (10 ppm) produce infertile eggs. Human beings are not seriously affected because they eat smaller amounts of food, and also a certain amount of their food may be imported and not grown locally. Mild selenium poisoning causes stunted growth, anorexia and gastrointestinal disturbances.

In South Africa numerous species of plants in the Karoo area have been found to contain dangerous amounts of selenium, and a correlation has been demonstrated between selenium content of the vegetation and the incidence of geeldikkop and enzootic icterus (Brown and de Wet, 1967); these two conditions at present are economically the most important ovine diseases in South Africa. The publication of Watt and Breyer-Brandwyk (1962) gives illustrations of geeldikopp and details about the disease.

Nitrates

A number of plants growing under certain soil conditions have been found to contain dangerous amounts of nitrate (salt-peter) and nitrite (Steyn, 1960; Watt and Breyer-Brandwyk, 1962), for example Sudan grass, barley hay, grass hay, oat hay, wheat hay, cornstalk, pigweed (*Amaranthus*), mint or mint-weed (*Salvia reflexa*) and *Tribulus* (duwweltjie). Rape, swedes, (rutabagas), turnips, beets and certain other vegetable material have caused serious losses in pigs and other animals from nitrate poisoning. Beets, broccoli, cabbage, cauliflower and lettuce may contain appreciable amounts that may at times be toxic to man. The nitrate content of spinach varies between 40 and 2100 mg per kg; nitrite poisoning has occurred in infants who had eaten spinach (Simon, 1966). Nitrates are reduced to nitrite in the gastrointestinal tract and these convert hemoglobin to methemo-globin. Thus, certain plant foods may occasionally cause methem-oglobinemia. However, it would appear that in contrast to rumi-nants the risk of acute or chronic poisoning from naturally-oc-curing nitrates in vegetables is very low (Fassett, 1966). (Nitrates in drinking-water have also caused poisoning; see Water.)

Estrogens

Estrogenic activity has been demonstrated in a number of plants and edible oils used as foods (Stob, 1966). Soybeans con-tain three isoflavone compounds which are weak estrogens. The amount of estrogenic activity present in plants and in certain ani-mal products (liver, egg yolk, milk) is so small that a physiologi-cal effect in man is virtually impossible.

Oxalates

Certain plants containing oxalic acid, usually in the form of acid potassium oxalate, have occasionally given rise to fatal poi-soning when used in cooking or for medicinal purposes (Watt and Breyer-Brandwyk, 1962).

Normally 80 to 90 per cent of oxalate in the diet is not ab-sorbed but is eliminated in the feces as insoluble calcium salts. Urinary oxalate is mostly endogenous in origin.

Oxalic acid forms insoluble calcium salts and is not easily absorbed from the intestine; its presence in food rarely causes ill effects. It can inhibit the absorption of calcium; however, the soluble oxalate present in food is seldom sufficient to have any practical influence on the absorption of calcium. A good review of this subject is given by Fassett (1966).

The oxalic acid content (mg per 100 gm fresh edible uncooked portion) of certain foods is given in the following list. There is great variation in the values given by different authors. The following are representative values. Fuller details are presented by Watt and Breyer-Brandwyk (1962), *Documenta Geigy-Scientific Tables* (1962), and Davidson and Passmore (1966). Foods other than those mentioned, and also prepared beverages such as tea, coffee and cocoa, contain little or no oxalic acid.

Rhubarb	100 - 900
Spinach	320 - 900
Celery (stalk)	620
Almond	407
Plantain (green)	517.5- 524
Plantain (ripe)	2.2
Sorrel	100 - 500
Cashew nut	318.4
Parsley	100 - 200
Beetroot	100 - 200
Currants	25 - 100
Prunes	25 - 100
Beans	25 - 100
Soybean	77

Potassium

Patients who are using oral diuretics may need to receive potassium to correct a hypokalemic state. Apart from pharmaceutical preparations, certain foods are recommended because of their high content of potassium. The following list gives an indication of the amount of potassium present in some foods of plant origin (mg per 100 gm) as given in *Documenta Geigy-Scientific Tables* (1962).

```
Yeast, brewers (dried) _____ 1900
Apricots (dried) _____ 1700
Molasses _____ 1238
Peaches (dried) _____ 1100
Dates (dried) _____  790
Figs (dried) _____  780
Peanuts _____  740
Raisins _____  708
Almonds (dried) _____  690
Beans, lima (fresh) _____  680
Cashew nuts _____  560
Bananas _____  420
Orange juice (fresh) _____  190
```

The amounts of potassium present in certain other foods are as follows: milk (dried) 1100; meat extract 1500; beef (dried) 1000.

Thiooxazolidones

A number of plants contain an antithyroid (goitrogenic) principle which has been identified as 1-5-vinyl-thiooxazolidone. It has been found in high concentration in extracts from the seeds of most *Brassicae* and in the edible parts of rutabaga and turnip. Tables giving the results of studies on antithyroid potency of various foods in man, and the thiooxazolidone content of seeds of plants of the mustard family, are presented by Greer (1957); an account of many dietary goitrogens of minor importance is given by Wills (1966). Some further details in connection with this subject are considered in a later section of this book dealing with cabbage.

Enzymes

These are organic catalysts produced by living cells. They consist of protein or contain protein as an essential part. Only a few examples are mentioned here.

Raw soybean contains proteolytic activity; six enzyme fractions have been demonstrated. It also contains trypsin inhibitor, and a number of other substances (see Soybean). Papain is a proteolytic enzyme or mixture of enzymes present in the juice of the pawpaw (papaya), the unripe fruit of *Carica papaya*. Bromelain (bromelin) is a proteolytic enzyme (or enzymes) derived from the pineapple plant. Tomatoes and some other higher plants elaborate enzymes which are able to degrade pectins.

Lectins

This term is applied to plant agglutinins, phytoagglutinins, differing in kind as judged by their effects on red blood cells (Boyd, 1963). These proteins are present in a great number of plant seeds such as castor bean (ricin), lima bean, soybean, and jack bean (Liener, 1966). They are present also in some cases in other parts of the plant. The castor bean and insufficiently cooked legumes have occasionally produced toxic effects when eaten. A large number and variety of pharmaco-active substances other than those mentioned above are present in foodstuffs of plant origin. These are considered in the following sections. Among these foods of plant origin are many that are customarily regarded or accepted as food but which sometimes prove harmful. Consideration is also given to certain plants that are recorded as being poisonous but which have mistakenly or unwittingly been eaten as food by persons lacking knowledge of the dangers.

ACKEE FRUIT

This is the fruit (ackee or akie) of a tree (*Blighia sapida*) common in the West Indies and South America, and brought to these areas from West Africa where the fruit is called isin (ishin). It has been regarded as a cause of an acute and very fatal condition, acute toxic hypoglycemia ("the vomiting sickness of Jamaica"). The clinical aspects are described by Stuart *et al.* (1955), Patrick *et al.* (1955). Some details about this fruit are given by Locket (1957), Manson-Bahr (1966) and Van Veen (1966).

When mature and in good condition the pear-sized fruit is wholesome enough. Unripe unopened fruit (with its attractive bright pinkish-red outer pod) and injured fruit are poisonous and should be avoided. The symptoms that have been reported include sudden onset of abdominal pain and vomiting, with apparent recovery; this is followed some hours later by severe vomiting, now of "cerebral" type, convulsions, coma. Death may occur in two to twelve hours from the onset of poisoning. The mortali-

Ackee

ty incidence is 80 to 90 per cent. At autopsy there are no characteristic changes demonstrable.

The fruit contains hypoglycin A and hypoglycin B, water-soluble poisons, which may be responsible for severe hypoglycemia possibly through an action on the liver.

These hypoglycins are not polypeptides. Hypoglycin A is a simple natural 7-carbon amino acid, α-amino-β (2-methylene-cyclopropyl) propionic acid; and hypoglycin B is a dipeptide, N-glutamyl hypoglycin A.

$$CH_2 : C - CH \cdot CH_2 \cdot CH \cdot COOH$$
$$\diagdown \diagup \qquad \qquad |$$
$$CH_2 \qquad \qquad NH_2$$

Hypoglycin A

$$CH_2 : C - CH \cdot CH_2 \cdot CH \cdot COOH$$
$$\diagdown \diagup \qquad \qquad |$$
$$CH_2 \qquad \quad HN \cdot CO \cdot CH_2 \cdot CH_2 \cdot CH \cdot COOH$$
$$\qquad \qquad \qquad \qquad \qquad \qquad \qquad |$$
$$\qquad \qquad \qquad \qquad \qquad \qquad \qquad NH_2$$

Hypoglycin B

The pharmacological actions of the hypoglycins of ackee have been studied in a variety of laboratory animals by Chen *et al.* (1957; 1961). These workers found that the hypoglycemia and fatty metamorphosis produced in the liver in certain species resembles that caused by synthalin, phalloidin and α-amanitin, and that other viscera also undergo changes; emesis produced in certain animals has no relation to the hypoglycemia. The relationship between diet and the acute toxicity of hypoglycin A in rats has been studied by Feng and Kean (1955).

Many authors have doubted whether ackees are wholly or even partly to blame for "toxic hypoglycemia"; other toxic agents may produce similar effects in certain circumstances (Fistein, 1960; Teelucksingh and Symonds, 1962).

ALMONDS

The bitter and sweet varieties of almond contain from 40 to 55 per cent fixed oil, about 20 per cent proteins, also mucilage and emulsin. The bitter almonds contain amygdalin in addition.

Bitter almonds contain 2.5 to 4 per cent cyanogenetic glycoside amygdalin, and the enzyme emulsin that hydrolyses it to release cyanide; it yields 0.5 to 0.8 per cent essential oil containing 4 to 7 per cent of hydrogen cyanide, HCN. Amygdalin is decomposed in two stages by the enzymes amygdalase and prunase found in emulsin;

$$\underset{C_{20}H_{27}O_{11}N}{\text{amygdalin}} + H_2O \xrightarrow[\text{amygdalase}]{} \text{prunasin} + \text{glucose}$$

$$\text{prunasin} + H_2O \xrightarrow[\text{prunase}]{} \underset{C_7H_6O}{\text{benzaldehyde}} + HCN + \text{glucose}$$

The seeds of stone fruits such as almond, plum, peach, cherry, apples, jetberry bush and toyon contain cyanogenetic glycoside which releases cyanide on digestion. The fatal dose for a small child varies from five to twenty-five seeds; adults also may be poisoned (Watt and Breyer-Brandwyk, 1962).

Almonds (dried) may be used to supply potassium in persons who have hypokalemia caused by oral diuretics; they contain 690 mg per 100 gm.

The ingestion of coco de mono almonds in large amounts can produce nervousness, anxiety and other features including loss of hair (Blood and Rudolph, 1966); the toxic mechanism is unknown.

APRICOT

Apricot (seed) (kernel) poisoning has occurred occasionally when too many kernels have been eaten. When crushed and moistened there is a release of cyanide from amygdalin and symptoms develop in one-half to two hours (Watt and Breyer-Bradwyk, 1962; Sayre and Kaymakcalan, 1964).

The ingestion of ten to twenty dried apricot kernels caused cyanide poisoning in a girl six years old. Her intake of hydrocyanic acid was estimated as 14-28 mg (Deichmann and Gerarde, 1964).

Dry apricots contain potassium 1700 mg, also calcium 86 mg, phosphorus 119 mg, and vitamin A 7430 units per 100 gm.

ASPARAGUS

There are many species of the genus *Asparagus;* a few are cultivated as food. The plant contains a variety of substances including sugars, acids, potassium salts, asparagin, resin and glycosides. The plant has been much used for a great variety of medicinal purposes. The diuretic action may be due to a phenolic glycoside, saponin, or organic acids. References to the medicinal uses are given by Watt and Breyer-Brandwyk (1962).

BAMBOO SHOOTS AND ATRIPLICISM

Fatal poisoning may occur when uncooked or even pickled bamboo shoots are eaten, due to the presence of large quantities of hydrocyanic acid (Locket, 1957). The following wild food plants have been recorded as causing poisoning.

The genus *Atriplex* is characterized by a high content of sodium chloride. The leaf of certain species and the young shoots are eaten by man. Certain species are stated to be useful as a fodder plant, but there has been poisoning in sheep, presumably due to hydrocyanic acid released from a cyanogenetic glycoside (Watt and Breyer-Brandwyk, 1962) .

The young shoots and the leaves of *Atriplex littoralis* cause sudden itching and tingling of the hands, edema, bullae and ecchymoses, often gangrene of the fingers, cyanosis and edema of the face and eyelids and occasionally jaundice. This has occurred particularly in North China and may be a photosensitization reaction. The disease must be distinguished from Raynaud's disease and erythromelalgia.

Atriplex patula (common orache) eaten instead of green vegetables for a number of weeks has caused weakness, edema of the face and hands, and yellow pigmentation of the skin.

Chenopodium album (fat hen) has also been eaten as a spinach in several countries. It occasionally produces poisoning (Scheuer-Karpin, 1948). Details of the chemical composition are given by Watt and Breyer-Brandwyk (1962).

BANANAS

Bananas contain large amounts of dopamine noradrenaline, and 5-hydroxytryptamine (serotonin) (Waalkes *et al.*, 1958); Udenfriend *et al.*, 1959; Marshall, 1959; Foy and Parratt, 1960) especially in the peel or skin. Their ingestion may lead to an erroneous diagnosis of carcinoid tumor or pheochromocytoma by producing increased urinary excretion of 5-hydroxytryptamine and noradrenaline and their metabolites (Crout and Sjoerdsma, 1959).

Endomyocardial fibrosis is a common form of heart disease, for example in Uganda, attributed to malnutrition and poor socioeconomic conditions. An interesting suggestion has been made that the ingestion of foodstuffs containing large quantities of 5-hydroxytryptamine (serotonin) might be an important cause of this fibrosis (Arnott, 1959) (*cf.* the fibrotic heart lesions of carcinoid heart disease; Ojo and Parratt, 1966). The plantain, a coarse type of banana, is one such foodstuff; the 5-hydroxytryptamine intake of many African peoples for whom plantains are a major article of diet may possibly reach 200 mg a day. The hypothesis has been questioned (Crawford, 1963; Brockington *et al.*, 1967). The 5-hydroxytryptamine may be one of a number of contributory factors, and may perhaps only be important when the mechanism in the body for detoxication of this indole amine is incapacitated.

The approximate concentration of amines present in bananas and plantains is as follows (amounts expressed as mg per 100 gm fresh fruit).

Bananas (peel)	Serotonin	5-15	Noradrenaline	12.2
	Dopamine	70	Tyramine	6.5
Bananas (pulp)	Serotonin	2.8	Noradrenaline	0.2
	Dopamine	0.8		
Plantains (ripe)	Serotonin	4-10		
Plantains (green)	Serotonin	2.6	Noradrenaline	0.2

Bananas (fresh) also contain potassium 420 mg per 100 gm, and many other substances in small amounts. In parts of tropical Africa an alcoholic drink known as banana beer is prepared from bananas (Simmonds, 1960).

BEANS

Castor Bean (*Ricinus communis*)

This contains the toxalbumin ricin in the seed but not in the oil expressed from the seed. It is very irritant. A child has died after ingesting five beans and an adult after ingesting twenty beans, but two seeds may also be a fatal dose for an adult (Watt and Breyer-Brandwyk, 1962). There is a latent interval of many hours and even days before symptoms develop. The features include severe gastroenteritis, hemorrhages and drowsiness; confusion, collapse, convulsions and coma may occur. The horse and sheep are very sensitive to the poison (Watt and Breyer-Brandwyk, 1962).

Fava Bean (Vicia fava), the Broad Bean or Horse Bean

These beans have commonly caused a hemolytic anemia known as favism in Sardinia, Italy and Sicily, also in neighboring areas, and in other countries including the United States. Fresh or dried cooked beans, and even the ingestion of a single bean, may within one to three days induce a severe intravascular hemolysis. Inhalation of the pollen of the plant may produce the following features in two or three hours: headache, gastrointestinal symptoms and severe hemolytic anemia. Sensitive persons have a deficiency of glucose-6-phosphate dehydrogenase (G-6 PD) in their red blood corpuscles, but there are other aspects to be considered (Liener, 1966). This hereditary enzyme defect is estimated to be present in more than 100 million people. Persons with this trait may also develop hemolytic anemia after taking certain drugs such as primaquine, phenacetin, probenecid, nitrofurantoin, sulphonamides, and certain vitamin-K preparations.

Broad beans containing dihydroxyphenylalanine (dopa) and dopamine (Hodge *et al.*, 1964) have caused hypertensive episodes in patients receiving antidepressant drugs of the mono-amine oxidase inhibitor type (see Cheese).

Lima Bean (Phasiolus lunatus)

This bean varies in color from pale pink with purple spots which type is known as the Rangoon bean, to pale cream or white which variety is called lima bean. Other names are Java bean and Burma bean. The white cultivated variety has not been recorded as causing poisoning.

Poisoning may occur especially from the colored varieties of the bean; the dark purple bean may yield as much as 0.1 per cent or more hydrocyanic acid from the cyanogenetic glycoside phaseolunatin $C_{10}H_{17}O_6N$ (Liener, 1966) which is identical with the cyanogenetic glycoside isolated from bitter cassava and linseed.

The highest amounts of cyanide that have been found in these beans are as follows (Montgomery, 1965); the amount of HCN is expressed as mg per 100 gm.

Java, colored	312
Puerto Rico, black	300
Burma, white	210
Jamaica, speckled white	17
Arizona lima, colored	17
American lima, white	10

Soybean (Soya Bean)

Raw soybean has proteolytic activity (Review, 1967). Raw soybean meal produces poor growth in chicks, due possibly to a trypsin inhibitor (antitrypsin factor), or a toxic principle, or to proteins the animals are unable to digest. Trypsin inhibitor and hemagglutinin are toxic factors important in interfering with the nutritive value of soybeans but are also present with other substances in a number of other varieties of beans such as navy beans (Review, 1964; 1966; Mickelsen and Yang, 1966). Trypsin inhibitors have also been found in many other legumes, in wheat flour, and in certain other foods (Ambrose, 1966). In some cases the nutritive value of the food protein is improved by autoclaving.

Soybean oil is an edible oil and has been tried in the treatment of atherosclerosis. Soybean and its oil contain three very weak estrogens called genistein, genistin and daidzein (Stob, 1966). The hemagglutinins present in soybean and certain other legumes are considered by Liener (1966).

BETEL NUT

The chewing of betel nut, with added tobacco leaf, has been incriminated as a cause of a highly differentiated squamous carcinoma of the cheek; this occurs mostly in the buccal sulcus where the individual habitually lodges the bolus when not chewing (Ahlumalia and Duguid, 1966).

BUCKWHEAT

There is a belief (doubtful) that buckwheat seed eaten as a cereal during summer months may cause a rash due to sensitization to light. Animals fed on the plant *Fagopyrum esculentum Moench.* do not develop the disease (fagopyrism) when kept stabled in semidarkness, but exposure to sunlight may cause pulmonary and intestinal hemorrhages, enteritis and emaciation (Queries and Minor Notes, 1955; Watt and Breyer-Brandwyk, 1962).

CABBAGE, AND PLANT GOITROGENS

Certain *Brassica* species eaten by man may cause severe irritant gastrointestinal and other symptoms (Watt and Breyer-Brandwyk, 1962). Cabbage and other plants of the genus *Brassica* have long been know to act as goitrogens in animals, causing hyperplastic thyroid glands devoid of colloid (Greer, 1957). However, goitrogens are present in vegetables in such low concentrations, except in seeds, that it is doubtful whether human beings would eat enough of such foods for goiter to be produced. Also, cooking destroys the goitrogenic potency. The goitrogenic plants possess sulphur-containing substances that may inhibit the formation of thyroid compounds. These antithyroid substances are known to exist in such foods as cabbage, turnip, brussel sprouts, and in the milk of cows fed on large quantities of kale during the winter. Goiter may be produced in rabbits by feeding them on a diet consisting mainly of cabbage. Mustard seed and rape seed are also able to induce goiter in experimental animals.

Thiourea   Goitrin

Cabbage seed, rape seed, mustard seed, turnip and swede roots and certain other edible plants have been shown to contain the precursor of goitrogenic agent, a cyclized thiocyanate, which is 1-5-vinyl-2-thiooxazolidone known as goitrin. It prevents the synthesis of organic iodine compounds in the thyroid gland. The thiooxazolidone content of the seeds of a large number of plants of the mustard family is given by Greer (1957).

Cabbage contains a thioglucoside named glucobrassicin (*cf.* the thioglucoside in cress) which on enzymatic cleavage yields thiocyanate, indole acetonitrile and 3-hydroxymethyl indole. Thiocyanate ion is a goitrogen, but the effect of these substances in man and animals remains to be studied.

Glucobrassicin   3—hydroxymethyl indole

There is no evidence that goitrin or thiocyanate is transferred to cow's milk in an amount that will affect the human thyroid. In linseed the goitrogen is a thiocyanate which prevents uptake of iodine.

Foods which contain thiocyanates do not cause goiter because the diet normally contains enough iodine to prevent their effects and insufficient thiocyanate-containing food is eaten to cause the effect. Also the precursors of the goitrogenic oxazolidones are inactivated during cooking which destroys the enzyme necessary to convert them to goitrogens.

In addition to the goitrogens in food there are goitrogens in water in certain areas. Also, there is the well-estabished fact that iodine deficiency in water and food can lead to the development of simple or endemic goiter, and in certain countries where this problem exists prophylactic measures have long been instituted. It has been suggested that in countries where iodine intake is low, for example in the Lebanon, the consumption of onions may contribute to goiter (Saghir *et al.*, 1966) .

In addition to the above-mentioned goitrogens there are many other dietary substances of minor importance that can cause enlargement of the thyroid (Wills, 1966). Probably the most potent of all is goitrin; it is a more potent goitrogen in man than prophylthiouracil.

CARROTS

The ingestion of carrots in large amount over a prolonged period, or of other foods containing the organic pigment carotene $C_{40}H_{56}$ (the precursor of vitamin A) such as sweet potatoes, mangoes, papayas and yellow squashes, can cause hypercarotenosis (carotenemia; carotenoderma) . There is an increase of the pigment in the blood and canary-yellow discoloration of the skin especially on the face, palms and soles. The sclerae are not affected which is a feature distinguishing the condition from jaundice. Carotenoderma has been observed in a six-month-old suckling whose mother ate several carrots daily (Thomson, 1943) . The phenomenon may also be observed in certain diseases such as diabetes, hypothyroidism and liver disorders where there is disturbance in the conversion of carotene to vitamin A. It is of interest that carotenoids are used as feed additives in the poultry industry to improve the pigmentation of egg yolks as well as the skin and shanks of poultry receiving insufficient carotenoids in their feed. Discoloration of the skin of a more orange-yellow color may be produced by the carotenoid lycopene in tomatoes.

The composition and uses of the carrot plant are given by Watt and Breyer-Brandwyk (1962). Poisoning by the plant is unknown, but the repeated ingestion of carrots which contain insecticide can cause toxic effects in man.

CASHEW NUTS

These nuts are the seed kernel of *Anacardium occidentale L.* They are poisonous unless roasted until all the pericarp oil is driven off. The oily juice is irritating as are the fumes that come off during roasting. The swollen fruit-stem (cashew apple) is also edible, and beverages both alcoholic and nonalcoholic are made from it. Details about the constituents of cashew nuts are given by Watt and Breyer-Brandwyk (1962). Cashew nuts contain potassium, 560 mg per 100 gm.

CLOVER AND LUCERNE

Spoiled or damaged sweet clover has caused poisoning in stock (Review, 1962). The first indication may be bleeding from the nose, and other features follow such as a stiff jerky gait and swellings of various sizes on the body due to extravasations of blood. Severely affected animals may die from hemorrhage. This condition is caused by the anticoagulant known as dicoumarol which is present in spoiled clover.

Lucerne is used extensively as a fodder plant. The fresh plant can produce severe tympanites, and death may occur from distention of the rumen or stomach pressing on the diaphragm and the large blood vessels. Much work has been done to elucidate the mechanism of bloat production. Poisoning may also occur from contamination of lucerne by some other truly poisonous plant material. Fuller details regarding poisoning by these plants eaten by animals are given by Watt and Breyer-Brandwyk (1962).

CRESS

Lepidium africanum DC. var. Capense Thell. (Cape cress, pepper cress, pepper grass) is used as a vegetable, and is eaten by stock. A sulphur-containing oil has been isolated from it. There is a report that it is poisonous. *Lepidium draba L.* (hoary cress, white top [USA]) is similar, but its leaf has been found to contain hydrocyanic acid and sulphoraphane MeCO $(CH_2)_4$ NH.C(:S) NHR which is identical with isothiocyanate present in savoy cabbage. *Lepidium myriocarpum Sond.* is used as a vegetable. *Lepidium sativum L.*, the ordinary cress (watercress, garden cress), and Indian cress (*Tropaeolum majus*) are also used as vegetables in various parts of the world. They contain a number of substances, for example a volatile oil known as cress oil which contains benzylisothiocyanate $C_6H_5CH_2NSC$ which passes through the body unchanged. Benzylisothiocyanate and benzyl cyanide are derived from benzyl thioglucoside by enzyme action when the plant tissue is crushed. About 10 mg of benzyl cyanide is derived from 30 gm garden cress, but whether this can cause harmful effects has not been established.

Benzyl thioglucoside

Benzyl isothiocyanate
HSO_4^- + glucose

Benzyl cyanide

Nasturtium officinale R. Br. (watercress, bronslaai) is sometimes used in salads, and the juice and seed as a kind of mustard. The plant contains vitamins A, C and D and many other substances such as a volatile oil and a glycoside (gluconasturtin). It is allegedly abortifacient and aphrodisiac, and has many uses other than an article of diet. Fuller details about the various species of cress are given by Watt and Breyer-Brandwyk (1962) and Strong (1966).

CYCAD SEEDS

Cycad seeds or kernels, also called cycad nuts, are obtained from *Cycad circinalis L.,* a palmlike tree, one of a number of species of Cycadaceae which are widely distributed throughout the tropics and subtropics. At least ten different species are used as food, especially in the Pacific area. They are a source of starch often used as food (Whiting, 1964). Ill effects may occur from cycad flour if it has not been properly prepared.

Ground unwashed cycad seeds (kernels) are extremely toxic and produce various effects in experimental animals, such as malignant tumors in the liver and kidneys (Mickelsen and Yang, 1966); cycad flour prepared by soaking in water removes the carcinogenic substance (Yang *et al.,* 1966). The type of tumors and their distribution resemble those produced by nitrosamines. Toxic substances isolated from cycad and related species *Macrozamia* are azoxy glycosides such as cycasin and macrozamin, in which the aglycone, methylazoxymethanol, is the toxic (carcinogenic) moiety (Laqueur *et al.,* 1963; Laqueur, 1964; Strong, 1966). The glycoside cycasin in cycad meal is decomposed to the aglycone by bacterial enzyme action.

$$CH_3 \overset{\overset{O}{\uparrow}}{N}=NCH_2-O-glucose$$

Cycasin

$$CH_3-\overset{\overset{O}{\uparrow}}{N}=NCH_2-O-primverose$$

Macromazin

$$CH_3\overset{\overset{O}{\uparrow}}{N}=NCH_2OH$$

Methylazomethanol

The aglycone resembles chemically the synthetic carcinogen dimethylnitrosamine which causes hepatic tumors in rats (Magee and Schoental, 1964; Proceedings of the Third Conference, 1964; Bonser, 1967). It is likely that this aglycone is also transformed

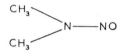

Dimethylnitrosamine

to an alkylating agent *in vivo* (Miller and Miller, 1966). A similar mechanism has been suggested for hepatocarcinogenic *Senecio* alkaloids.

Cycad meal may be contaminated with fungi that produce mycotoxins such as aflatoxins, so that carcinogens both from the meal and the fungi may be the cause of liver cancer and other malignancy in people who eat this food (Petering, 1966). The toxic factor from cycad meal is excreted in the milk of the mother, as is the case with aflatoxins, and it can cross the placenta.

FIGS

There are many species of fig. Most of their fruit is edible although not so palatable as that of *Ficus carica L.* It contains about 50 per cent sugar which is chiefly glucose, appreciable amounts of vitamin A and C, smaller amounts of B and D, and small amounts of acetic, citric and malic acids, and a proteolytic enzyme known as ficin. The proteolytic action varies a good deal according to the species of fig. It is probably responsible for some degree of anthelmintic action claimed for the fig in folk medicine. Ordinarily, fig is a mild laxative. Dried figs have a high content of potassium, 780 mg per 100 gm, and may be used as one of the sources of this element in persons who have hypokalemia induced by oral diuretics.

Ficus carica is one of the plants liable to induce a photosensitization skin reaction (*cf.* buckwheat) due to hypersensitivity to some chemical constituent in the plant. It differs from contact dermatitis. The photosensitizing agents would appear to be fluorescent principles such as ficusin belonging to the coumarin or furo-coumarin group. The reaction is characterized by the sudden onset of itching and burning in the skin twenty-four to forty-eight hours after exposure to the plant and the sun. Linear wheals and bullae then develop on an area of erythema, varying in size from a few millimeters to a few inches in diameter. Deep purple pigmentation may follow, which may persist and even become permanent. Some details of the constituents of various species of fig and the uses of many parts of the plants for medicinal and other purposes are given by Watt and Breyer-Brandwyk (1962).

GARLIC (KNOBLAUCH)

This is the fresh bulb of *Allium sativum* used as a seasoning agent and an article of food. It has also been widely used as a folk remedy for the prevention and treatment of a variety of diseases (Watt and Breyer-Brandwyk, 1962).

The active principle, garlic oil, consists principally of diallyldisulphide and allyl propyl disulphide, but there are other substances also present in the plant. Alliin is an odorless compound from which allicin is derived. Only the allicin has the typical odor of garlic, and also an antibacterial action. Both compounds have been synthesized by Stoll and Seebeck (1947) (Laboratory report, 1953). The amount of alliin present in garlic

$$
\begin{array}{ccc}
CH_2 & & CH_2 \quad CH_2 \\
\parallel & & \parallel \qquad \parallel \\
CH & & CH \quad\; CH \\
\mid & & \mid \qquad\; \mid \\
CH_2 & \text{Alliinase} & CH_2 \quad CH_2 \\
\mid & & \mid \qquad\; \mid \\
S \rightarrow O & & O \leftarrow S \underline{\qquad} S \\
\mid & & \quad\; \text{Allicin} \\
CH_2 & & CH_3 \\
\mid & & \mid \\
H_2N{-}CH & & 2CO + 2NH_3 \\
\mid & & \mid \\
COOH & & COOH \\
\text{Alliin} & &
\end{array}
$$

varies according to the site where the plant is grown. This compound is a previously unknown amino acid. It is acted on by an enzyme alliinase which degrades the sulphur-containing amino acids. For further details the review given by Watt and Breyer-Brandwyk (1962) may be consulted.

Special preparations have been used for a variety of medical purposes, but they should not be given to children in whom they are dangerous. Fatalities have been recorded.

GUMS, MUCILAGES AND PECTINS

Acacia (Gum Arabic), Sterculia (Gum Karaya) and Tragacanth

These gums can be ingested in large amounts, but may produce diarrhea, flatulence, and rarely impaction of feces. Occasionally an allergic reaction occurs.

Acacia consists mainly of arabin, the calcium (with traces of magnesium and potassium) salt of arabic acid. It also contains diastase and an oxidase system. Tragacanth contains tragacanthin and bassorin.

In South Africa many species of *Acacia* are of importance as animal feed. Some have occasionally been found to yield hydrocyanic acid. They have also been used by primitive peoples for a variety of medicinal purposes (Watt and Breyer-Brandwyk, 1962).

Agar

This is the dried colloid mucilaginous substance extracted from certain red marine algae. It consists mainly of an indigestible long-chain polysaccharide of complex structure which gelatinizes with water; it also contains 1 to 2 per cent protein. Agar has little nutritive value and passes through the intestine virtually unchanged. It takes up water and increases the volume of the feces, in this way promoting peristalsis. Plantago seed (psillium seed) is similar. Information about agar is given by Watt and Breyer-Brandwyk (1962).

"Bubble gum" consists mainly of synthetic rubber, polymers and flavoring additives. Ingestion of large quantities may lead to the formation of bezoars (Deichmann and Gerarde, 1964).

Pectin (Pectic Acid)

Plant pectins are very similar to the gums and mucilages. They are polysaccharides found in many fruits, young green plants and root vegetables, for example turnips.

Pectin is obtained as a purified carbohydrate from apple pulp (apple pomace) or from the inner portion of the rind of citrus fruits. It consists chiefly of partially methoxylated polygalacturonic acids. In water it forms a viscous colloidal solution.

It has been used for a variety of purposes, for example commercial pectin in the manufacture of jams and jellies. At one time raw apple was used in the treatment of enteritis in infants, the pectin probably absorbing toxins.

Pectin is stated to reduce the clotting time of blood and has been employed as a hemostatic orally or as a compress (*Extra Pharmacopoeia*, 1967). In man pectin can produce a decrease in serum cholesterol. This appears to be related to a decrease in the absorption of cholesterol and to reabsorption of bile acids (Review, 1966).

In fowls the addition of pectin to the diet reduces the incidence and severity of spontaneous and cholesterol-induced atherosclerosis. This is probably due to acceleration of the passage of food through the alimentary canal (Fisher *et al.*, 1966).

HEMLOCK

Ingestion of this plant (*Conium maculatum*), the spotted hemlock, has caused hundreds of deaths in man, because of the resemblance of the leaves to parsley, the roots to parsnips and the seed to anise. Apparently boiling does not destroy the toxicity. Symptoms of poisoning are identical with those caused by the volatile alkaloid coniine. There is burning sensation in the nose and throat, dysphagia, twitching, tremor, ataxia, weakness, also salivation, dilatation of the pupils, fibrillation of the muscles and loss of consciousness. Death may occur within three or four hours from respiratory failure at the height of a convulsion (Locket, 1957; Dewberry, 1959).

The water-hemlock (*Cicuta virosa L.*) (*Cicuta maculata*) cowbane, and the water dropwort (*Oenanthe crocata L.*), another member of the hemlock family, have also been eaten and caused poisoning. The seeds of the water-hemlock resemble anise and the root may be mistaken for wild parsnip or Jerusalem artichoke;

symptoms of poisoning include vomiting, violent convulsions, and sometimes death occurs from the "cicutoxin." Dropwort root has been mistaken for parsnip, and the crushed leaves smell like celery. Symptoms of poisoning include delirium, convulsions, and death may occur within a few hours after eating the root which contains a nonalkaloidal poison called oenanthotoxin (Dewberry, 1959).

The parsnip (*P. sativa*) and several of the parsley plants (*Petroselinum hortense*) contain myristicin (*cf.* nutmeg).

HONEY

Purified honey obtained from the comb of the hive bee contains 70 to 80 per cent glucose and fructose, sucrose, dextrin, wax, proteins, volatile oil, formic acid and water. Pollen grains and other matter present in suspension tend to induce fermentation. Adulterants likely to be present in commercial honey are artificial invert sugar, sucrose and liquid glucose.

Honey has been the cause of poisoning when collected by bees from toxic plants. Symptoms are usually gastrointestinal but occasionally disorientation and convulsions have occurred (Locket, 1957). Certain rhododendrons (including azaleas), melianthus, nerium oleander, datura and various euphorbias have been the source of poisonous honey (Steyn, 1949), as well as some other plants (Blood and Rudolph, 1966).

Honey and honeycombs may contain fumigants such as calcium cyanide, ethylene dibromide, methyl bromide and paradichlorobenzene (Gleason *et al.*, 1963). In the treatment of bees for disease, antibiotics must be limited with regard to their use and the season of administration, so that the antibiotic will not get into the honey intended for sale (Sarsikov, 1966).

Royal jelly and honey are the natural food of bees. The jelly is believed to be produced by the salivary glands of worker honey bees, and is essential for the development of queen bees. It contains proteins, lipids, carbohydrates, fatty acids and vitamins (Dayan, 1960), an antibiotic and acetylcholine (Colhoun and Smith, 1960); Brown and Felauer, 1961; Christensen, 1962), a tumor-inhibiting principle 10-hydroxy-2-decenoic acid (Townsend *et al.*, 1961), nucleotides (Marko *et al.*, 1964), and insulinlike activity (Dixit and Patel, 1964). An account of the biologically active substances in the jelly is given by Rembold (1965). There is no evidence from animal experiments that it can affect growth, longevity, or fertility in man.

Mead (honey wine or honey beer) may have a sugar content of 5 to 10 per cent, and alcohol 10 per cent, but brandy has been added to it to increase the alcohol concentration to 20 per cent.

HORSERADISH

This substance which is used as a condiment is the fresh root of *Armoracia rusticana* (= *A. lapathifolia*). It is credited with containing the glycoside sinigrin (*Extra Pharmacopoeia*, 1967). However, it was shown by Heiduschka to contain allylthiocarbamide ($C_4H_8N_2S$ = 116.2) and not sinigrin (Watt and Breyer-Brandwyk, 1962).

JENGHOL SEED

The seeds (fruit pods and beans) (djenkol beans) of the plant *Pithecolobium lobatum* have a foul smell due to volatile sulphur compounds. They resemble the horse chestnut and are eaten with relish as a food by the inhabitants of certain parts of Indonesia, in spite of their toxic properties. They contain an amino acid known as djenkolic acid, and they have a high vitamin-B content.

Strangury, oliguria, albuminuria and renal colic can occur, in severe cases resembling an acute abdominal emergency. The urine frequently contains blood casts, and sharp acid crystals of

$$H_2C \Big\langle \begin{array}{l} S - CH_2 - CHNH_2 - COOH \\ S - CH_2 - CHNH_2 - COOH \end{array}$$

Djenkolic acid

djenkolic (jengcolic) acid. The presence of these crysals in large numbers in the urethra causes necrosis, fistula and extravasation.

The breath and urine acquire a foul smell characteristic of the seeds. Death has occurred.

Some details about these beans are given by Locket (1957), Manson-Bahr (1966) and van Veen (1966).

LICORICE

This substance which is used as a sweetmeat is obtained from the root of *Glycyrrhiza glabra*. It also has other uses, for example as a demulcent and as a mild purgative. Incidentally it is of interest that it is much used in the tobacco industry. Some pipe tobaccos contain up to 10 per cent, and snuff may contain more. A review of the pharmacology and chemistry of licorice was published by Nieman (1957).

Licorice may sometimes contain an active principle, the 18-beta isomer of glycyrrhetinic acid, which has mineralocorticoid, antidiuretic and anti-inflammatory action. This is not surprising in view of the chemical structure of the compound (Molhuysen *et al.*, 1950; Parke and Williams, 1962). In large doses licorice has caused salt and water retention leading to hypertension and severe electrolyte imbalance, because of its cortisone-like properties. It has produced hypokalemic myopathy with myoglobinuria (Gross *et al.*, 1966). Intoxication with licorice has also been reported to produce hypokalemia, paresthesiae, paresis, hypertension, tetany, polyuria and alkalosis (Meyler, 1966).

Glycyrrhetinic Acid

Carbenoxalone sodium (disodium enoxolone succinate) (biogastrone) is prepared from glycyrrhetinic acid present in licorice root and is used to hasten healing of gastric, but not duodenal, ulcers; it also is liable to cause retention of sodium and water and loss of potassium, especially in elderly patients or in those with incipient heart failure.

MAIZE

This grain (*Zea mays L.*) is also known as corn or Indian corn, and in South Africa as the mealie. It is much used as a food.

Poisoning has sometimes occurred in cattle and other animals that have eaten the plant. This has been attributed to the presence of hydrocyanic acid, potassium nitrate, or a parasitic fungus such as *Aspergillus* and *Ustilago* growing on the plant. Cornstalk disease occurring in cattle in the United States has been attributed to similar factors and to bacterial poisoning. A review of this problem is given by Watt and Breyer-Brandwyk (1962).

MANCHINEEL

The applelike fruit of this tree which grows in the West Indies, South America, Central America and Florida closely resembles the crab apple. If the fruit is eaten, it causes swelling of the lips and mouth, vomiting and dysentery. Death has occurred in a few cases (Earle, 1938). The irritant principle is a resinous substance, possibly euphorbone.

Hypersensitive people who pick the manchineel apples may suffer from a skin eruption; erythema, bullae, and vesiculation may occur. Conjunctivitis may result from the introduction of the latex into the conjunctival sac. Some details about this fruit are given by Manson-Bahr (1966).

MANGO

This fruit (*Mangifera indica L.*) contains ascorbic acid, carotene, tannic acid, a fixed oil and a pigment mangiferin. There are irritants in the skin of the fruit that can produce dermatitis and gastrointestinal symptoms. The peel should not be eaten.

The eating of excessive amounts of the fruit has been known to cause carotenemia and renal inflammation. Details about the constituents in the fruit, leaf, stem, bark and root of the plant and other information are given by Watt and Breyer-Brandwyk (1962).

MANIOC (CASSAVA)

This is an important food for numerous people in the tropics (Jones, 1959). There are many varieties, some being very poisonous because of the presence of the cyanogenetic glycoside phaseolunatin (see also Lima beans).

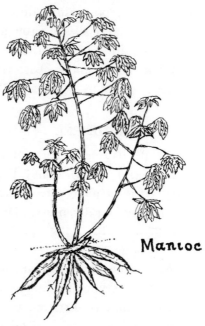

Manioc

The bitter manioc (*Manihot utilissima*) must be distinguished from the sweet variety (*Manihot aipi*) which is a source of tapioca starch used as a staple food. The customary distinction between "bitter" and "sweet" varieties rests upon the content of hydrocyanic acid in the edible parts of the roots. The raw plant contains a soluble cyanogenetic glycoside amygdalin which releases hydrocyanic acid and causes cyanide poisoning when the root or tuber is damaged or soaked in water. Most of the glycoside and its enzyme are present in the outer coat (rind) of manioc root which can easily be removed as a peel. Cassava is improved when grated and sun-dried, a procedure done traditionally, as this leads to elimination of the hydrocyanic acid from the glycoside.

The features of poisoning, which come on suddenly, are giddiness, headache, confusion, loss of consciousness and stertorous breathing. Vomiting may occur. Convulsions may precede death which usually follows within two hours but may be delayed for a longer period.

Details of the constituents of this plant and of poisoning are available in the publications of Nicholls (1961), Watt and Breyer-Brandwyk (1962) and Montgomery (1965). According to a compilation of the last-named author the highest reported yield of cyanide (HCN mg per 100 gm) from bitter cassava is as follows.

Whole root	55
Stem	113
Root cortex	65
Dried root cortex	245

MANNA

Manna (manna from heaven; bread of heaven) is sweet like honey. It is well known from interpretation of biblical and other accounts as the secretion exuded by tamarisk trees and bushes, for example when the stems are pierced by a certain type of plant-louse as for instance on the Sinai Peninsula. The manna ash is a small tree of common occurrence in the Mediterranean area, and the food is almost entirely collected from certain species of the tree, for example in Sicily from *Fraxinus ornus*.

Manna is yellowish white, brittle and sticks to the teeth. It contains 40 to 60 per cent mannitol $C_6H_8(OH)_6$ which is a hexa-

$$
\begin{array}{c}
CH_2OH \\
|\\
HOCH \\
|\\
HOCH \\
|\\
HCOH \\
|\\
HCOH \\
|\\
CH_2OH
\end{array}
$$

D—Mannitol

hydric alcohol closely related to the hexose sugars. It also contains 10 per cent water, 2.2 per cent glucose, 2.5 per cent fructose,

6 per cent mannotriose, 12 per cent mannotetrose, 0.05 per cent resin, and the fluorescent glycoside fraxin. It has mild laxative properties but it may cause flatulence and griping.

MARMITE

This is a commercial, flavored concentrated autolyzed protein-free yeast extract; salt-free Marmite is also available. It contains riboflavine 1.5 mg, and nicotinic acid 16.5 mg per ounce.

In nutritional megaloblastic anemia Marmite may elicit a response in the bone marrow with the production of new red blood cells (Vinke, 1964). The response is usually not adequate. The hematinic action is due partly to folic acid in the extract. It is not produced by ordinary yeast.

Marmite also contains substances such as tyramine and histamine which can enter the general circulation from the intestine when mono-amine oxidase inhibitors such as the antidepressant drug tranylcypromine are being taken. Severe hypertensive episodes can occur (Blackwell, Marley and Mabbit, 1965). Tyramine in cheese and certain other foods has also caused such episodes.

The chemical composition of compressed baker's yeast and dried brewer's yeast is given in *Documenta Geigy-Scientific Data* (1962). Brewer's yeast though rich in vitamins is too bitter as an adjunct to most diets.

Dried yeast is used in man as a source of the vitamin-B group, and a number of other substances including enzymes, for the prevention and treatment of vitamin-B deficiency diseases. Large doses may cause diarrhea. It is also employed as a dietary supplement for pigs and poultry and other animals. Large amounts of yeast may produce a rachitogenic effect; they may also decrease the amount of vitamin A in the liver. Details about these and other antivitamin effects in animals are given by Lepkovsky (1966).

Yeasts should never be given unless they are well cooked or in the form of Marmite, as live yeasts can deplete the thiamine (aneurine) in the diet by absorption of the vitamin or by destroying it by enzyme (thiaminase) action (Nicholls, Sinclair and Jelliffe, 1961).

MARROWS, SQUASHES, MELONS

Bitter and poisonous forms of the cultivated species of these and other *Cucurbitaceae* have sometimes caused serious poisoning and even death. Bitter and toxic principles known as cucurbitacins have been isolated. The review given in Watt and Breyer-Brandwyk (1962) should be consulted for details of the chemical constituents and poisoning, and for references to the literature on this subject.

MUSHROOMS

There is a general idea that all fungi except mushrooms are to be regarded with suspicion and that most are poisonous. In fact a good many are edible, most are harmless but not worth eating, and only a few are poisonous. An account of the use of mushrooms and toadstools as food is given by Ramsbottom (1953) and Stephens and Kidd (1953).

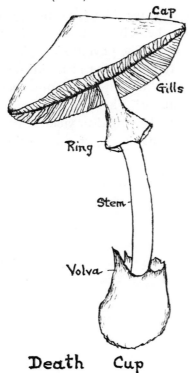

Death Cup

There are several common inedible, distasteful, though non-poisonous fungi about which questions are frequently asked, for example the purple-stemmed russula, the orange tuft, the sulphur Tuft and Dye Balls.

The ill effects caused by mushrooms may be due to (a) allergic hypersensitivity; (b) simple indigestion; (c) stale or altered mushrooms, and (d) specific poisoning by toxic species (Stephens and Kidd, 1953; Dewberry, 1959; Watt and Breyer-Brandwyk, 1962; see also the references below).

Mushroom poisoning of severe degree is produced only by a limited number of species, but it has occurred very often. Most dangerous are the death cups, the hepatotoxic fungi, such as *Amanita phalloides L.* and the Cape toadstool or Cape death cup, *Amanita capensis* (Sapeika, Uys and MacKenzie, 1960). They have white gills, a white collar and white cup at the base of the stem.

Numerous bicyclic peptides have been demonstrated in *A. phalloides,* most of them being toxic (Wieland and Wieland, 1959; Wieland, 1963). The phytotoxic cyclopeptides such as the less toxic but more rapidly acting phalloidins and the more toxic amanitins are composed of only a few amino acids, some of which do not occur in proteins. They are resistant to enzymes. Fresh fungus *A. phalloides,* 100 gm has yielded 10 gm of phalloidin ($C_{35}H_{46}O_{10}N_8S$ + $6H_2O$), 8 mg of α-amanitin, 5 mg of β-amani-

	R_1	R_2	R_3
Phalloidin	OH	CH_3	CH_3
Phalloin	H	CH_3	CH_3
Phallacidin	OH	$CH(CH_3)_2$	COOH

tin, and about 0.5 mg of y-amanitin. Phalloidin is stated to be nontoxic but is transformed into an active compound by enzymes present in the liver. The chemical constituents of *A. capensis,* a fungus thus far only found in the Cape Peninsula (South Africa) have not been determined.

Among other poisonous mushrooms there is *Amanita mus-caria* (the fly agaric) which contains muscarine and sometimes myceto-atropine. These alkaloids are quite different from the cyclopeptides present in the death-cup fungi from the chemical point of view and in their pharmacological and toxic effects.

$$HO-CH-CH_2-CH_3 \quad H_3C-O-CH_2-N^+(CH_3)_3$$

Muscarine

There are no simple tests that will differentiate toxic and nontoxic varieties of mushroom. Lay persons have used simple, fanciful but dangerous, methods for distinguishing poisonous from nonpoisonous varieties, but the only way is to know them and to distinguish them as one does other edible plants.

Symptoms of Mushroom Poisoning

These may develop rapidly, or may be delayed.

ONSET IN FIFTEEN MINUTES TO TWO HOURS. *Amanita mus-caria* (the fly agaric) contains muscarine which has a cholinergic action; on the other hand in certain parts of the world it may contain atropine-like compounds (myceto-atropine) which has an anticholinergic action. *Amanita pantherina* (the panther) is similar. The symptoms will be different according to which con-stituents are present, and there is the important point regarding treatment: atropine is an antidote for muscarine alkaloid, but is contraindicated in myceto-atropine poisoning. These mushrooms cause burning pain in the stomach, vomiting, diarrhea, drunken delirium and finally a state of stupor and deep sleep, but rarely death.

Poisonous inocybes for example *Inocybe eutheles, Inocybe hirtella* and *Inocybe obscura* contain muscarine, and produce profuse sweating, lachrimation, salivation, constriction of the pupils, coughing, difficulty with respiration, slowing and weakening of the heart. Belladonna tincture and atropine are antidotes. Recovery should occur in twenty-four hours.

The copper trumpet (*Clitocybe olearia*), poison pie, green-lined parasol (*Lepiota morganii*), the yellow-staining mushroom and related varieties may produce vomiting, diarrhea, intense thirst and shock.

A number of fungi, for example *Psilocybe mexicana* and *Stropharia cubensis,* are eaten by Mexican Indians during religious ceremonies for the effect of the psychotomimetic or hallucinogenic constituents (*cf.* cannabis which also is eaten or smoked for the sensation which it produces).

ONSET IN FIVE TO FIFTEEN HOURS. The death-cup fungi are mostly responsible for serious poisoning and death, and cause symptoms after a latent period; death follows progressive damage to the liver. Representatives in this group are *Amanita phalloides, A. capensis, A. brunnescens* and *A. verna.* These have been responsible for most fatalities. There is no antidote for these hepatotoxic fungi although a toxin antiserum (of unproven therapeutic value) has been described, and is reputedly available only at the Pasteur Institute in Paris, France (Block *et al.,* 1955). Hemodialysis has been used with success in an anuric patient (Elliot *et al.,* 1961).

THE *Clitocybe* SPECIES. The agaric genus *Clitocybe* includes a very large number of named species. The majority have been regarded as generally nontoxic and even as good eating. A few species are reported as being poisonous to man, causing unpleasant symptoms of transient nature, but at least two species (*Clitocybe dealbata* and *C. rivulosa*) are toxic and have caused death, and *C. sudorifica* produces profound sweating. The features are stated to be identical with those produced by *Inocybe* and *Amanita muscaria* which are rarely causes of death, but very little is known about the chemical and pharmacological features of these fungi (Sapeika, 1965).

The occurrence of *p*-methyl nitrosaminobenzaldehyde in an "edible" mushroom *Clitocybe suaveolens* (Preussman *et al.,* 1964) indicates that nitrosamines can be formed under natural conditions. Burrell *et al.* (1966) have investigated a close association between esophageal cancer and poor plant production and consider that deficiencies in certain plants may lead to the formation of nitrosamines, some of which can cause cancer. Molybdenum deficiency may be responsible for accumulation in certain plants of nitrate and oxides of nitrogen which can react with secondary or tertiary amines to produce nitrosamines. Specific nitrosamines tend to induce cancer at specific sites, irrespective of the route by which they are administered. A number of agents of this class have been shown to induce esophageal cancer in laboratory animals. This is important in the current search for nitrosamines or other agents in the environment which induce esophageal and other cancers in man.

Esophageal cancer is endemic among the Bantu population in South Africa, especially in the Transkeian region, not generally but in isolated, well-defined pockets. In these the morbidity rate for squamous carcinoma of the thoracic esophagus may exceed 1 per 1,000 of the population each year, whereas in surrounding areas the disease is not seen. In some of these pockets the disease is more or less confined to males, in others to females. The disease has been increasing in incidence since it first became prevalent in 1943 (Burrell, 1959; Burrell, 1962; Burrell *et al.,* 1966). Similar increases have been observed among the Bantu in other regions of South Africa. White persons and Asians living in the affected areas have not been involved in the increasing incidence of the disease. The male Bantu may be exposed to special cancer hazards. One hazard is "cidivici," beer illicitly brewed, sometimes in metal drums which previously contained petroleum asphalt, and sometimes with the addition of carbide or metal polish. The consumption of "foods' such as the prickly vine tips from pumpkins and various edible weeds by persons dependent on gardens with poor yields, or of fungal toxins (see Aflatoxins), have been suggested as other possible causes for the esophageal cancer (Annotation, 1966).

Inky cap (*Coprinus atramentarius*), a black-spored mushroom, has no toxic effects unless it is combined with the ingestion of alcohol. It may then cause flushing, palpitation, dyspnea and other features well known to occur when alcohol is taken after the drugs disulfiram (Antabuse®) $(C_2H_5)_2N.CS.S.S.CS.N (C_2H_5)_2$ and calcium carbimide (dipsan, temposil, absten) $(CaCN_2)$. These agents are used in the aversion treatment of chronic alcoholic subjects. A report of four cases of toxic reaction to alcohol following the ingestion of *C. atramentarius* is presented by Reynolds and Lowe (1965). It should be noted that List and Reith (1960) were unable to confirm that this fungus produces tetraethylthiuram disulphide (disulfiram), but found it contains many other substances. It is also of interest that other mushrooms of the genus *Coprinus* do not cause this type of poisoning.

MUSTARD

Black mustard seeds contain a glycoside (sinigrin) which when crushed and moistened with water undergoes hydrolysis by an enzyme (myrosin). A volatile oil is produced, the main active constituent of which is allyl isothiocyanate (C_3H_5NCS). White mustard seeds contain a glycoside (sinalbin) which is chemically related to sinigrin, and the enzyme myrosin; it yields the analogous oil acrinyl isothiocyanate. These "volatile oils of mustard" are irritant to mucous membranes, and if taken internally in large amount they cause vomiting.

White mustard seeds also have a cathartic action which has been attributed to the liberation of H_2S when they come in contact with water, and large doses may produce sulphide poisoning. Similar sulphur-containing oils are formed in certain other plants such as cress, radish, horseradish, and in garlic and onion.

Mustard seeds contain goitrogens. This is considered in another section (see Cabbage).

NUTMEG

This is the dried kernel of the seeds of the nutmeg tree which has long been used as a spice to give character and stimulus to food. It yields from 5 to 15 per cent volatile oil and 30 to 40 per cent fat, also phytoserin, starch, amylodextrin, coloring matter and a saponin. The volatile oil contains pinene and camphene, dipentene, alcohols, myristicin, safrole, eugenol and isoeugenol. The oil of mace is almost indistinguishable from that of the nutmeg.

Myristicin has been shown to have psychotropic properties in human beings ((Shulgin, 1966), but it seems as yet unproven that the action of nutmeg can be fully ascribed to this compound (Weil, 1966).

Myristicin

Serious but rarely fatal poisoning may be caused in adults from the ingestion of one to one and a half nutmegs, or from one teaspoonful of powdered mace. Finely ground nutmeg or the oil has been taken on many occasions as an abortifacient and has caused severe symptoms (Green, 1959). The features of poisoning occur in one to six hours. There may be depression or central nervous stimulation and gastrointestinal symptoms (Blood and Rudolph, 1966). Recovery is usually complete in twenty-four hours. For some case reports the *Extra Pharmacopoeia* (1967) and books on toxicology may be consulted. It has been stated that there is a possibility of some degree of liver damage. Noteworthy is the close relationship in chemical structure between myristicin and safrole; the latter compound causes hepatotoxic and even hepatocarcinogenic effects when administered to rats.

OAK

The leaves of the oak (*Quercus*) has been used in stock feeds, for example for pigs, but preferably mixed with other food. As an exclusive diet it is insufficient to maintain weight. Continuous feeding produces sickness and sometimes death in a small percentage of animals, but not if the animal eats other food in sufficient quantity.

The eating of acorns by young animals may also result in poisoning that may prove fatal. Acorns contain up to 7 per cent tannic acid, but this does not appear to be the only harmful constituent. Moldy acorns are certainly harmful. The nutritive value of acorns is stated to be about half that of maize. Details with regard to this subject are given by Watt and Breyer-Brandwyk (1962).

Preparations made from acorns are alleged to create an aversion for alcohol, also to control constipation or diarrhea associated with the drinking of alcohol.

OILS AND FATS OF VEGETABLE ORIGIN

Fixed oils and fats of vegetable origin are mainly triglycerides, i.e., esters of glycerol with the fatty acids oleic, palmitic and stearic acids. They occur mainly in the endosperm or embryo of the seed except in the case of olive oil and palm oil which are obtained from the fresh pericarp of the fruit.

These substances do not exert any marked pharmacological action. Many of them are edible, for example olive oil and cottonseed oil. They are digested and serve as food of high caloric value. A few produce pharmacological actions when ingested; for example in castor oil the triglyceride of ricinoleic acid acts as a purgative (after being hydrolyzed by intestinal lipase to glycerol and the irritant ricinoleic acid). Olive oil and cottonseed oil are laxative if given in large amount. The eating of unaccustomed rich food cooked or fried with excessive amounts of fats or oils is one possible cause of "traveller's diarrhea" occurring during visits to other countries particularly Mediterranean, Arabic and Latin American countries. Colic, malaise and repeated watery stools (without blood) are the features of this particular condition. Some toxic materials that may be present in frying oils have been identified (Review, 1960).

Unsaturated fatty acids occur in large amounts in the oils and fats of certain seeds, such as linseed and sunflower seed, and in some animal fats. These acids and oils containing them have been given to lower blood-cholesterol levels in patients with hypercholesterolemia. This subject is considered in another section (see Dietary Factors and Blood Lipids).

Arachis Oil (Peanut Oil, Groundnut Oil)

This fixed oil consists of glycerides, the fatty acid components of which are chiefly oleic and linoleic acids with smaller amounts of palmitic, arachidic, lignoceric and stearic acids. It has properties similar to olive oil and is used for the same purposes. Emulsions containing 10 per cent oil and 40 per cent dextrose are administered by intragastric drip as a nitrogen-free diet. Peanut oil does not contain aflatoxin which therefore does not reach margarine (Review, 1962; see also Peanuts).

Cottonseed Oil

This oil has properties and uses similar to those of olive oil. Cottonseed oil emulsion has been given intravenously as a food to provide calories in the treatment of severe nutritional deficiency, but there is risk of toxic reactions immediately and delayed. Contaminated cottonseed meal has been suspected of causing a high incidence of hepatomas in hatched trout (Wolf and Jackson, 1963; Review, 1964; see also Peanut meal).

The toxicity of cottonseed meal associated primarily with its content of a toxic pigment, gossypol, will not be considered here. Most of the cottonseed meal available in commerce has had the gossypol removed during processing and is sufficiently free of this agent to be safe for use. A useful review of gossypol and other substances in cottonseed meal that affect the growth of animals and the quality of hens' eggs is given by Eagle (1966) and by Mickelsen and Yang (1966). Attempts are being made to develop genetic strains of cottonseed which will be devoid of gossypol.

Linseed Oil

This oil is obtained from the seeds of flax, and contains glycerides of linoleic, myristic, oleic, palmitic and stearic acids. It is digestible and nutritious but large doses are laxative. Much of the commercial oil type has a marked odor and an acrid taste. Linseed cake which still contains some oil in addition to the proteins and mucilage is a valuable cattle food, but it has caused death from cyanide poisoning (Watt and Breyer-Brandwyk, 1962).

Boiled linseed oil is dangerous and should never be taken internally as it may contain toxic elements such as cobalt, lead, or manganese, resin, resin oils and other fixed oils.

Sesame Oil

This oil also contains glycerides of higher fatty acids, and 1 per cent sesamin which is a complex cyclic ether. In large amounts it is laxative as with other fixed oils.

Some persons are hypersensitive to sesame seed, and severe reactions can occur with features such as oral and glossal pruritus, general erythema, edema of the uvula, shock and wheezing (Torsney, 1964). The seed may be present in biscuits and confections.

Contaminated Oil

Cooking oil contaminated with airplane engine oil containing orthocresylphosphate was responsible for thousands of cases of poisoning in Morocco in 1959 (Godfrey, 1961; Travers, 1962). This was similar to the outbreaks of poisoning occurring in the United States in 1930 from the consumption of certain brands of Jamaica ginger extract adulterated with triorthocresylphosphate (jake paralysis or ginger paralysis) (Annotation, 1960). There have also been deaths from its presence as a contaminant of soft drinks and other drinks, and of oil of apiol. There is a latent period of one to ten days when peripheral neuritis develops leading to bilateral foot and wrist drop; the lesion is motor, and the legs especially are involved. Harmful effects that may be produced by contaminated oil and meal of linseed and cottonseed are considered above.

ONIONS

The onion *Allium cepa L.* has caused fatal poisoning in horses and cattle, possibly from decay in the onion. The various species of *Allium,* including onion, garlic, leek and chive, possess sulphur-containing volatile oils which are irritant; onion and garlic may cause contact dermatitis. Poisoning in animals has been characterized by gastrointestinal and urinary symptoms; anemia and jaundice may also occur. The ingestion of onion by cows may result in the milk having an unpleasant taste. Onion, like garlic, has been used for many medicinal purposes (Watt and Breyer-Brandwyk, 1962).

The lachrymatory factor in onions is propenyl sulfenic acid, which with cycloalliin is derived by enzymatic action from the precursor propenyl cysteine sulfoxide.

Propenyl   Propenyl-L-cysteine   Cycloalliin
sulfenic   sulfoxide
acid

The physiological effects of the various sulphur compounds isolated from members of the onion and the cabbage families have not been extensively examined. In certain countries where the iodine intake is low, for example in the Lebanon, onions may be goitrogenic (Saghir *et al.,* 1966).

PEANUTS

Peanuts are seeds of a leguminous plant *(Arachis hypogoea),* and are also known as groundnuts and monkey nuts. They resemble other pulses in general nutritive value, but are very rich in fat. The whole seed contains about 50 per cent oil. Groundnut cake is excellent cattle food, and the oil is used for cooking purposes or for making margarine.

Peanuts contain a factor which prevents and controls bleeding and produces clinical improvement in some cases of hemorrhagic disease, possibly due to an action on capillaries (Boudreaux and Frampton, 1960; Annotation, 1960). Peanut flour has been tried with some success in the treatment of hemophilia (Bisordi, 1964). It is thought to act by inhibiting fibrinolysis (Mainwaring and Keidan, 1964).

Peanut (Groundnut) Meal and Aflatoxins

Peanut meal imported from Brazil, East and West Africa, and India has produced harmful effects in turkey poults, ducklings, chicks, pigs, calves and sheep. In Britain alone in 1960 thousands of turkeys died from this cause (Sargeant *et al.*, 1961; Review, 1962). An outbreak in pigs was described by Loosmore and Harding (1961). The disease has been shown to be due to "aflatoxin" which is usually a mixture of four structurally related metabolites named aflatoxins B, B_1, G, G_1, of which B_1 is usually found in greatest amount and appears to be most toxic. These toxins are produced by certain molds such as the common fungus

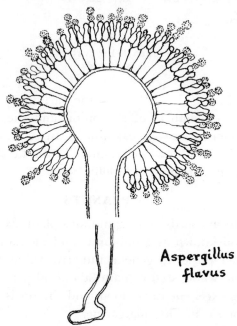

Aspergillus
flavus

Typical head showing sterigmata in two series

Aspergillus flavus (Cheung and Sim, 1964); other toxins are also produced by this fungus (Wilson, 1966). Aflatoxins and other mycotoxins can be present in many cereal products and are not restricted to peanut or cottonseed meals. There is considerable difference in the effect of the toxins on different animal species.

The aflatoxins represent one group only of a large number of toxins produced by *Aspergillus* fungi; others include for example the toxins present in *Penicillium islandicum* (see Rice), and sterigmatocystin which is a metabolite of a species of *Aspergillus versicolor*.

Important nutritional and agricultural aspects of mycotoxicosis have been studied and reported, for example at a symposium in South Africa (1965), and a symposium in Canada (1966). A considerable number of these mycotoxins, some of them carcinogenic, have been isolated in pure form in many laboratories throughout the world (Kraybill *et al.*, 1964; Dickens, 1964; de Wit *et al.*, 1966; Holzapfel *et al.*, 1966; Lijinsky and Butler, 1966; Wogan, 1966). Schoental (1967) has reviewed the toxic and carcinogenic effects of aflatoxins, their metabolism and biochemical effects, and their possible importance as a cause of human liver diseases.

Typical histological features produced include fatty infiltration, liver-cell damage, and bile-duct proliferation. Changes in the liver resembling biliary cirrhosis have been produced in young rhesus monkeys (Tulpule *et al.*, 1964; Review, 1965) especially those on a low-protein diet (Review, 1967). In calves lesions of the centrilobular hepatic vein resembling those of veno-occlusive disease have been observed (Hill, 1963), a lesion previously regarded as pathognomonic for pyrrolizidine alkaloid toxicity. The significance of aflatoxin-induced hepatic injury in vitamin deficient baboons in relation to hepatic cirrhosis and carcinoma in Africans has been considered by Foy *et al.* (1966).

The guinea pig is very susceptible to the toxic effects of aflatoxin (Butler, 1966), and much investigation has been carried out on ducklings, rats, hamsters, birds, fish and other animals (Schoental, 1967). The aflatoxins are extremely potent hepatotoxins for ducklings, the LD_{50} being of the order of 15 to 20 μg for day-old ducklings. As little as 0.03 μg per gm of a 0.5 per cent toxic groundnut meal in a ration, fed over long periods, induces liver cancer in these animals. The toxicity of certain groundnut meals for ducklings and chickens has been investigated by Asplin and Carnaghan (1961), and the biochemical changes in liver tissue and blood from ducklings and chickens have been studied by Brown and Abrams (1965). Another mycotoxin named ochratoxin A has been shown to produce mild fatty infiltration of the liver (Theron *et al.*, 1966) and glycogen storage.

Aflatoxin B₁

Ochratoxin A

Aflatoxin B_1 ($C_{17}H_{12}O_6$) in a single dose in rats produces a slowly developing periportal parenchymal cell necrosis (Butler, 1964; Butler and Clifford, 1965). In the pregnant rat aflatoxin may cause retardation of fetal growth, probably secondary to the maternal liver damage (Butler and Wigglesworth, 1966). Malignant tumors have been produced in the rat liver by feeding certain peanut meals or aflatoxin for many weeks (Annotations [a] [b], 1962; Dickens and Jones, 1963; Diener *et al.*, 1963; Leading article, 1964; Review, 1964; Wogan, 1966). Aflatoxin B_1 is also carcinogenic in trout (Ashley et al., 1964) and ducks (Carnaghan, 1965; Wogan, 1966).

Aflatoxin inhibits DNA synthesis in the liver by preventing DNA polymerase from transcribing DNA and in turn inhibiting RNA polymerase. This causes interference with the genetic determinants of the cell (Rees, 1966).

Inhibition of the liver protein synthetic mechanisms and of RNA metabolism occurs within a few hours of administration of the toxin (Clifford and Rees, 1966), which appears to be correlated with disruption of the rough endoplasmic reticulum (Butler, 1966). Inhibition of DNA synthesis is probably due to a direct action of the DNA molecule (De Recondo *et al.*, 1966).

The acute toxic effects of aflatoxin on cell cultures and embryos have been described by a number of workers, for example by Zuckerman and Fulton (1966), and on lung cells by Legator (1966). Other references are given by Wogan (1966). Aflatoxins may induce chlorophyll deficiency (albinism) in plants (Schoental and White, 1965).

Possible Effects in Man

Peanuts for confectionery are hand selected, and this should ensure that moldy nuts are not included. There is no evidence that human beings have suffered acute illness from the consumption of groundnuts contaminated with aflatoxin or of products manufactured from such seeds, for example cooking oil and peanut butter, but long-term exposure to traces of this very active carcinogen must be considered as a possible cause of tumors at a later date. This hazard to human health merits very serious attention. The same applies to corn and other cereal grains contaminated with strains of *A. flavus* that produce a tremorgenic neurotoxic principle which causes tremors and convulsions in mice (Wilson and Wilson, 1964).

It has been suggested that the contamination of foodstuffs with mycotoxins in certain parts of South Africa may be related to the incidence of primary liver cancer in the Bantu (Oettle, 1965; Purchase, 1967). The experimental findings cited in the sections above have many parallels with liver disease in man. Veno-occlusive disease of the liver produced by *Senecio* alkaloids and "bush tea" resembles the Budd-Chiari syndrome (Selzer and Parker, 1951) and in the chronic disease is clinically indistinguishable from other types of cirrhosis. Seneciosis is considered in another section of this book dealing with bread poisoning. There are also tribal medicines known to be toxic and which can cause death from liver failure (Neame and Pillay, 1964). The incidence of hepatoma appears to be increasing in some countries, including England (Elkington *et al.*, 1963) and the possibility of "natural" hepatotoxins being the cause is being investigated.

It has been suggested that some fungal toxins are esophageal carcinogens, and must be considered in the etiology of esophageal cancer which is endemic among the Bantu population in South Africa; this problem is considered elsewhere (see Nitrosamines; Bantu beer). Persons exposed to aflatoxins and other mycotoxins, for exampe in laboratory investigations, should take precautions including procedures for decontamination and detoxication of the toxins (Harington, 1967).

PEAS

The seeds of *Lathyrus sativus L.* (chick pea) are species of tares or vetches which are pulses allied to beans and peas. They grow wild in India and certain other countries and are used as food and fodder. Poisoning and deaths have occurred in a number of animal species from lathyrus peas in the feeds, the horse being especially susceptible (Watt and Breyer-Brandwyk, 1962). They have caused disease ("lathyrism") in thousands of people (Nicholls, Sinclair and Jelliffe, 1961), also in livestock that have eaten large quantities. The disease has also occurred in France, Spain, Italy (*L. clymenum*), and in N. Africa (*L. cicera*), where these small peas are eaten. It also occurred in concentration and prison-of-war camps during World War II (Passios and Demopoulos, 1962). *L. odoratus,* the sweet pea of flower gardens, has caused poisoning ("odoratism") in children.

The medicinal significance of *Lathyrus* seeds and other seeds which are related to them is considered by Montgomery (1965) who points out that nitrile compounds with potent neurotoxic properties have been isolated from *Lathyrus* and *Vicia sativa* seeds. Their relevance in human neurolathyrism has not been estabished; other compounds appear to be more important (see below). Two syndromes have been associated with the consumption of lathyrus peas, as follows.

OSTEOLATHYRISM. In this condition, bone and mesenchymal tissues are primarily affected. There is a resemblance to various bone diseases such as osteogenesis imperfecta and to Marfan's syndrome. The features include deformities in bone, slipped epiphyses, dental anomalies, hernias and dissecting aneurysm. This disorder, osteolathyrism, has been the subject of much experimental study, as for example by Levene (1963) and Weaver and Spittell (1964).

The material identified in certain lathyrus species toxic for rats includes certain nitriles, for example beta-amino-propionitrile $NH_2CH_2CH_2CN$, but not in lathyrus species toxic to man. Beta-aminopropionitrile, which may be responsible for osteolathyrism, occurs mainly as the y-N-glutamyl derivative in *L. odoratus,* and in *L. hirsutus* and *L. pusillus* which have caused poisoning in stock in the southern United States (Strong, 1966).

$$HOOCCHCH_2CH_2CONHCH_2CH_2CN$$
$$|$$
$$NH_2$$

y−glutamyl−/β—aminonitrile

Studies in animals and man in regard to the metabolism of beta-aminopropionitrile and its effects as an inhibitor of collagen cross-linking, i.e., collagen maturation, have recently been reported by Keiser and Sjoerdsma (1967).

NEUROLATHYRISM OR HUMAN LATHYRISM. This condition is characterized by an insidious onset. The features that develop include pain in the back, weakness and spasticity of the leg muscles from involvement of the corticospinal tracts; there may be no sensory disturbances. In animals similar symptoms occur as well as other features. For illustrations see Watt and Breyer-Brandwyk (1962). Neurotoxic substances isolated from various species of lathyrus peas include α, y-diaminobutyric acid and beta-cyano-L-alanine (Review, 1963; Liener, 1966).

$$NH_2CH_2CH_2CHCOOH \qquad\qquad N\equiv C-CH_2-CHCOOH$$
$$|\qquad\qquad\qquad\qquad\qquad\qquad |$$
$$NH_2 \qquad\qquad\qquad\qquad\qquad NH_2$$

Diaminobutyric acid   /β—cyanoalanine

Rao *et al.* (1967) have isolated from *L. sativus* the unusual amino acid compound β-N-oxalyl-L-α, β-diaminopropionic acid $HOOC.CO.NH.CH_2.CH(NH_2)COOH$ which is claimed to be one of the principal neurotoxic factors. These workers have shown that it can induce neurolathyrism in monkeys. A review of some lathyrogens and related compounds is given by Strong (1966) and Liener (1966).

PEPPER

The number of fruits resembling pepper (*Piper* species) is very large. Such spices have flavor appeal (see Flavoring Agents) and stabilizing effects in foodstuffs. They are antioxidant in edible fats, and some have lipolytic activity, for example black pepper (Halbert and Weeden, 1966).

Black pepper is the dried unripe fruit of *Piper nigrum* used as a condiment. It contains alkaloids, namely the pungent resin chavicine (a compound of piperidine and chavicinic acid, piperine ($C_{17}H_{19}O_3N$) and piperidine, and 1 to 2.5 per cent volatile oil which consists largely of terpenes (phellandrene and dipeptene).

White pepper (*Piper album*) is obtained from black pepper; the fruits are allowed to become more completely ripe. It contains less volatile oil than the black variety.

Capsicum

The varieties of capsicum include African chillies, tabasco pepper and Louisiana pepper, which are used as a condiment known as cayenne pepper. Chillies contain about 0.14 to 0.22 per cent of the pungent principle capsaicin, ascorbic acid 0.1 to 0.5 per cent, red carotenoid pigments and fixed oil (Trease, 1961). The actions of capsaicin and its analogues are described by Keele and Armstrong (1964) and by Smith (1967).

$$OH$$
$$OCH_3$$
$$CH_2NHCO(CH_2)_4CH=CHCH(CH_3)_2$$

Capsaicin

Capsicum is irritating to skin and mucous membranes. When taken internally it can produce severe gastritis, vomiting and diarrhea and painful micturition.

Lethal doses of capsaicin cause a fall of blood pressure in which pulmonary vasoconstriction plays an important role (Molnar and Gyorgy, 1967).

Hungarian capsicum or "paprika" is a convenient source of ascorbic acid. Very large *Capsicum* fruits resembling tomatoes in texture and practically nonpungent are widely grown in South Europe as vegetables; there is doubt that these are distinct species or cultural varieties.

PINEAPPLES

This fruit is rich in ascorbic acid (vitamin C), and it contains a powerful proteolytic enzyme known as bromelain. Fresh and canned pineapple juice contain much 5-hydroxytrytamine (serotonin) (Bruce, 1961; Foy and Parratt, 1961), and after their ingestion there is excretion of 5-hydroxy-indole acetic acid (5-HIAA) (West, 1960).

The approximate concentration of 5-hydroxytryptamine in this fruit has been reported as follows (mg per 100 gm).

Pineapples (green) 5-6
Pineapples (ripe) 2
Pineapple juice 2.5-3.5

Toxic symptoms from eating the fruit has been reported from Hanoi; heart failure, cyanosis and ecchymoses have been followed by collapse, coma and sometimes death (Note, 1912). The unripe fruit is credited with many pharmacological properties (Watt and Breyer-Brandwyk, 1962).

POTATOES

Potatoes (*Solanum tuberosum*) may contain in green tubers and new sprouts small quantities of the poisonous glycosidal alkaloid solanine $C_{45}H_{73}NO_{15} = 868.1$. This substance is formed in parts of the potato with highest metabolic activity, i.e., under the skin and in the sprouts. It is a cholinesterase inhibitor, as is also its aglycone solanidine. The usual concentration of the alkaloid in sprouting potatoes (less than 0.01 per cent) is nontoxic. New potatoes may contain as much as several hundred milligrams per kilogram. When the amount exceeds 20 mg per 100 gm the potatoes are considered injurious. Symptoms of solanine poisoning appear about eight hours after a meal. There may be severe gastrointestinal symptoms (nausea, vomiting, diarrhea, tachycardia, dilated pupils and depression of the cardiovascular and respiratory systems). Recovery is usually complete, but confusion, coma and death may occur.

Anticholinesterase activity has been demonstrated not only in extracts of potato, but also in apples, broccoli, eggplant, oranges and a number of other vegetables and fruits (Crosby, 1966). Very little is known about the chemistry of cholinesterase inhibitors in food.

Potato tubers yield proteins that inhibit diverse proteolytic enzymes (Ryan and Huisman, 1967). In fact the storage organs of a large number of species of plants contain proteins that inhibit various animal, bacterial and fungal proteolytic enzymes; see also soybeans.

Certain chemicals have been applied to potatoes as antisprouting agents, for example waxing compounds such as the methyl ester of naphthalene acetic acid.

PRUNES

These are the dried ripe fruits of certain species of *Prunus domestica*. They exert a laxative action because they contain hydrophilic and mucilaginous material, and an irritant related to oxyphenisatin (dihydroxyphenylisatin); i.e., their action is due to bulk, emollient and irritant effects. Oxyphenisatin is chemically closely related to bisacodyl (dulcolax), and like the latter it acts directly on the colon stimulating muscle contraction.

The seeds contain hydrocyanic acid to an extent that they have been used in attempts to commit suicide (Watt and Breyer-Brandwyk, 1962). Other species of prunus such as apricot, cherry and peach also contain hydrocyanic acid in the kernel.

RHUBARB

Certain species of rhubarb cultivated in China and Tibet are used as anthraquinone purgatives. American varieties grown as vegetable plants are devoid of laxative action.

The leaves contain significant quantities of oxalic acid and oxalates, much more than rhubarb stalks. When boiled as greens they (and also the petiole) have uncommonly been the cause of serious symptoms and sometimes fatal poisoning. Fatalities have occurred in children from the ingestion of the leaves. The oxalate combines with calcium and can induce hypocalcemic irritability, twitchings, tremors and convulsions. Continued ingestion may cause the accumulation of insoluble oxalate crystals in the ureter and bladder to produce irritation, pain and hematuria, and renal damage may occur. Death may be due to renal obstruction.

Rhubarb, spinach and certain other foods should be eliminated from the diet of patients who have passed oxalate stones and gravel or urine containing large numbers of oxalate crystals.

RICE

In Japan, the incidence of primary liver carcinoma is stated to be increasing. A mold (*Penicillium islandicum*) which infects and produces yellowing of rice, so-called yellow rice or yellowsis, has been shown to produce metabolites that can cause liver damage in rats (Coady, 1964; Leading article, 1964; Feuell, 1966; Wilson, 1966). Cirrhosis and neoplasia can be produced, the latter a mixed cholangiocarcinoma and hepatoma or occassionally a sarcoma.

Islanditoxin   Luteoskyrin

Two distinct compounds have been isolated from cultures of *P. islandicum* (a) islanditoxin, an unusual chlorine-containing cyclopeptide which is a powerful hepatotoxin in experimental mice and rats, and (b) luteoskyrin, an anthraquinone derivative which is also a hepatotoxin but relatively slow acting. These two toxins, which have been shown to be carcinogenic, may be related to the occurrence of hepatoma in the Far East (Purchase, 1967). The "yellow rice" problem is complex. The high incidence of liver disease in the principal rice-eating areas of the world is complicated by the prevalence of dietary deficiency syndromes and other factors.

Other molds isolated from rice produce a variety of toxic metabolites (Wilson, 1966); for example *P. citrinum* produces citrinin which causes nephrosis in mice.

Citrinin

Japanese rice beer and rice wine (sake) is made by allowing the carbohydrate in rice to be converted to fermentable sugar by "koji," an *Aspergillus* mold. The sugar is then fermented by a *Saccharomyces* yeast (Leake and Silverman, 1966). Arrack may be made from rice, or from molasses or the juice of the coconut palm (see Alcoholic beverages).

SEAWEED

Much seaweed is used as human food especially in Eastern (Asiatic) countries, also as carrageen "moss" on the coasts of Scotland and Ireland, and generally in the coastal districts of most countries of the world. The constituents include alginic acid and its calcium, magnesium and sodium salts. This forms the main cell-wall constituent which is a hard, horny, indigestible polysaccharide consisting of *d*-mannuronic acid residue units joined by β-1:4-glycosidic linkages. The alginates have certain advantages over agar, starch, pectin, gums and gelatin. They are incorporated as thickening, emusifying and stabilizing agents in food, including ice cream, and for many other purposes. Other organic compounds and inorganic chemicals are also available such as laminarin, which is analogous to starch of land plants, mannitol, proteins in small amount (but important in the use of seaweed as a food for animals), fat, vitamins, pigments, iodine and a number of other substances (Trease, 1961). The proportion of the various constituents depends on species, season of the year, habitat, stage of growth and depth of immersion.

The seaweed Irish moss (*Chondrus crespus*) (carrageen) contains a gumlike substance known as carrageenin. Subcutaneous injection of this sulphated polygalactose in rats may produce sarcomata at the site of injection. Carrageenin has been used for a variety of purposes in the food industry, for example as an emulsifying agent for cod-liver oil and other oils, but there is no evidence that it induces cancer when administered orally in animals (Roe and Lancaster, 1964). The laxative effect of seaweed is due to organic sulphates, mannitol and fucoidin, in addition to the bulk provided by hydrophilic colloids (Watt and Breyer-Brandwyk, 1962).

Many seaweeds are rich in iodine, some of the kelps (*Laminaria*) containing as much as 1 part per 1000. More usually, there are 2 parts per million as in *Gelidium rigidum* which is rich in agar and used in the East to make jellies. Certain species are prescribed by the Chinese for goiter.

Agar is a dried colloidal substance prepared from various red algae, especially species of *Gelidium*. It is a long-chain polysaccharide of complex structure. It has little nutritive value. It acts as a bulk laxative when administered in the form of small pieces like bran; finely powdered or sandlike powder is not efficacious.

STRAWBERRIES

Strawberry extracts have been shown to contain histamine liberators. This may explain the sensitivity reactions, various types of allergic phenomena, including urticarial skin rashes and angioneurotic edema, that occur in some individuals after they have eaten strawberries.

TAMARIND

The wild tamarind (*Leucaena glauca* Benth.) or West Indian lead tree is a shrub or low tree cultivated in some countries. The leaf and unripe fruit are edible, as also the seed which yields starch and fat. Other substances are also present. The material is eaten almost regularly in certain parts of Indonesia.

Loss of hair occurs in animals and apparently in man following the ingestion of the flower, leaves and seed. The depilatory action is ascribed to the presence of an amino acid, mimosine $(C_4H_5O_2N)x$. Some details are given by van Veen (1966), who states that when the food is prepared in iron pots it is rendered harmless; also, that the action of mimosine may be due to interference with pyridoxal-5-phosphate compounds.

The plant takes up selenium from seleniferous soil and stores it, as do many other plants (see section Foods of Plant Origin). Selenium poisoning that occurs in animals may produce a condition known as blind staggers or alkali disease. Details about this plant poisoning and selenium poisoning are given by Watt and Breyer-Brandwyk (1962).

TOMATOES

Tomato juice taken in excess can produce a deep orange-yellow discoloration of the skin and lycopenemia because of the presence of carotenoid lycopenes (Arena, 1963). Lycopene accumulates in the liver, and illness has resulted from the chronic ingestion of large amounts of tomato juice (Reich *et al.*, 1960).

Tomatoes contain indole derivatives, for example tryptamine, and traces of 5-hydroxytryptamine (West, 1958, 1959; *cf.* bananas and pineapples). They also contain the bitter gluco-alkaloid solanine (Watt and Breyer-Brandwyk, 1962). They elaborate enzymes that are able to degrade pectins.

Wild tomato (bull nettle, horse nettle; sand briar; *Solanum carolinense*) contain solanine in the green fruit (*cf.* potatoes). It produces gastrointestinal symptoms and depression of the cardiovascular and respiratory systems.

TUNG NUTS

Tung nuts (*Aleurites fordii*) contain a sapotoxin in the seed. This irritant has caused gastrointestinal symptoms, weakness and hypotension in adults and children who have eaten the fruit kernels (Watt and Breyer-Brandwyk, 1962), and especially severe symptoms when the oil (tung oil; Chinese-wood oil) was used for frying fish (Huisman and Vasbinder, 1962). Cattle have been poisoned from grazing the foliage, also from eating trimmings and discarded foliage of the tree.

YAMS

The tubers of various *Dioscorea* species have been used as a food in certain countries. They contain alkaloids such as dioscorine, which is bitter, produces toxic effects resembling those caused by atropine, cocaine and picrotoxin, has local anesthetic and antidiuretic actions, and potentiates the action of adrenaline. Diosgenin which is a suitable precursor of the steroid cortisone has been isolated from several species; the South African species *Dioscorea sylvatica* has been used for cortisone production.

Diosgenin

Dioscorea alata (white yam; winged-stalk yam) is edible. It is said to produce narcosis when fresh but not when boiled or roasted. It contains yam starch.

Dioscorea bulbifera L. (potato yam) contains much starch and some saponin, and Mexican varieties contain diosgenin. *Dioscorea dregeana* contains alkaloids. It can produce a state of intoxication and paralysis of the legs if the tuber is eaten without having been soaked in running water for several days.

Dioscorea dumetorum Pax. (wild yam; bitter yam) contains toxic alkaloids, for example dioscorine and dihydrodioscorine, which can produce a drunken or convulsive state and other features. The tuber is nevertheless eaten in African countries, the Philippines and Java. It is made safe by soaking in water to extract the toxic principles, but there are also strains which are less bitter and less toxic.

Dioscorea elephantipes Engl. (Elephant's foot) is used as a food containing starch and sago. It also contains diosgenin.

An account of the above-mentioned tubers and other related species with some information on their constituents and their medicinal and other (toxicological) uses is given by Watt and Breyer-Brandwyk (1962).

WHEAT

BRAN. This is the husk of cereal grain, separated from the flour after grinding the grain. It contains 20 per cent cellulose which is indigestible, acts as roughage, and so promotes increased intestinal activity. It can act as a bulk-forming purgative. Large amounts are required to produce this laxative action which seems to depend not on the cellulose content *per se,* but on the physical condition or structure of the cellulose and other related indigestible polysaccharides in the bran which have power to retain water. The cellulose is effective in fibrous form but not as a powder (Review, 1960). Dried prunes, dried apples and dried figs are similar in these respects. They contain large amounts of indigestible material, most of which is cellulose.

In some individuals bran has an irritant action on the intestinal mucous membrane and produces diarrhea. It is not used when there is an inflammatory condition of the gastrointestinal tract. Also, it may increase the spasticity in "spastic constipation."

WHEAT FLOUR. This contains gluten which is therefore present in many foods, for example bread, many breakfast cereals, biscuits, cakes, pastries, macaroni, spaghetti and also some proprietary preparations such as Ovaltine®. It is also present in rye, oats and barley. Gluten is absent from pure wheat or rye starch, cornflakes, oatmeal porridge, rice, all fruits and vegetables and all meats. The significance of this lies in the fact that gluten, which is a mixture of the proteins gliadin and glutelin, is a toxic substance for certain persons (Review, 1964). Its presence in the diet of children with celiac disease, and in nontropical sprue, interferes with the intestinal absorption of neutral fat, carbohydrate, vitamin D and sometimes of iron, folic acid, vitamin-B complex and protein. Gluten or one of its proteins, gliadin, can produce the celiac syndrome in patients who have been in full remission on a gluten-free diet (Review, 1963). The basis of treatment is a gluten-free diet plus certain supplements.

Wheat gluten produces circulating antibodies (Mansmann, 1966); they develop in especially high concentration in certain diseases of the alimentary tract, as occurs with cow's milk proteins. A lack of correlation between the titers of maternal and cord blood is one conspicuous finding (Wright *et al.*, 1962).

Bread Mold

As a moist food, bread is capable of supporting the growth of a variety of molds, the spores of which are killed during baking. Post-baking contamination is from mold (spores) derived mainly from the atmosphere and includes species of *Cladosporium, Penicillium, Aspergillus, Mucor* and *Rhizopus*. These have a distinctive appearance or color, and a "musty" odor and flavor. There would appear to be no record of human disease from the consumption of moldy bread, but the formation by certain molds of toxins harmful to animals is an established fact. Much attention is being paid to aflatoxins and other mycotoxins as pointed out in other sections of this book.

Bread Additives

Among the many substances that have been used to improve the quality of bread are chlorine dioxide (as a bleaching agent and flour improver), potassium iodate (to improve the baking quality of flour), benzoyl peroxide (as a bleaching agent for white flour), mono- and di-glycerides of natural fatty acids (in the shortening used in bread), and polyoxyethylene stearate (as an anti-staling agent) (Steyn, 1953).

Bread Poisoning

A number of chemical compounds and plant substances have

been responsible for causing illness and death, occasionally on a big scale, from their accidental contamination of bread. Vermin poison such as strychnine or barium salts has sometimes been accidentally mixed in meal or flour. Fungicides applied to seed wheat have caused poisoning. For example hexachlorobenzene, not to be confused with gamma benzene hexachloride, has caused many cases of cutaneous porphyria in Turkey (Schmid, 1960; Dean, 1961; de Matteis *et al.*, 1961).

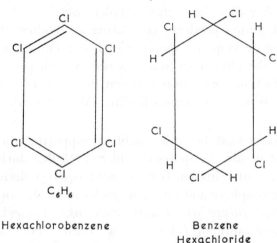

Hexachlorobenzene   Benzene
Hexachloride

A hemorrhagic disease known as alimentary toxic aleukia has occurred in many parts of Russia among people who ate bread prepared from grain, especially millet, that had been left unharvested and became moldy in the field during winter. The condition is a mycotoxicosis characterized by stomatitis and gastrointestinal disturbances that may be of temporary duration, but meanwhile leucopenia with relative lymphocytosis, and a decrease in red cells, hemoglobin and platelets occur. Hemorrhages and ulcerative processes come on rapidly if the toxic food continues to be eaten. The poison is derived from the fungus *Fusarium sporotrichiodes* and possibly from other molds. It is stable to ordinary domestic cooking and baking procedures but is removed or destroyed in commercial mills (Review, 1962). Three toxic principles have been described (Feuell, 1966); these are fusariogenin glycoside, epicladosporic acid and fagicladosporic acid.

Some details about *Fusarium* species and the fungal toxins are given by Wilson (1966).

A number of plants have been incriminated as a cause of bread poisoning; for example *Datura* species, *Ricinus communis*, *Argemone mexicana*, ergot (*Claviceps purpurea*), and various *Senecio* species.

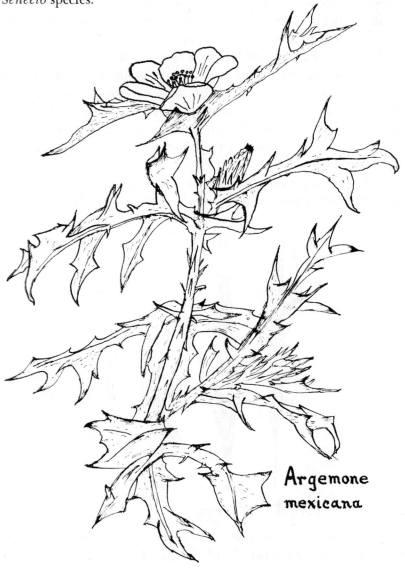

Argemone mexicana

The Mexican poppy or pricklypoppy (*Argemone mexicana*) growing on mustard fields in India (Nicholls, 1961) and on wheatlands in South Africa in the northwest Cape districts has caused poisoning (Steyn, 1950; Watt and Breyer-Brandwyk, 1962). Epidemic dropsy from damage to the capillary walls is produced by a poison in the seed of the weed; myocardiopathy has also been described (Brink *et al.*, 1965). Toxin from the seeds of this plant has also been present in mustard oil used as the chief cooking fat in Bengal and Behar and has been responsible for epidemic dropsy in these regions. This poppy weed commonly grows in the mustard crops. The seeds of the weed have been shown to contain an alkaloid, sanguinarine, which is toxic (Sarkar, 1948). It inhibits the oxidation of pyruvic acid and, as in wet beriberi, pyruvic acid may accumulate in the blood of patients suffering from epidemic dropsy.

Ergot is a parasitic fungus that grows on rye, wheat, oats and on certain other grasses. Ergotism is rare nowadays, but epidemics

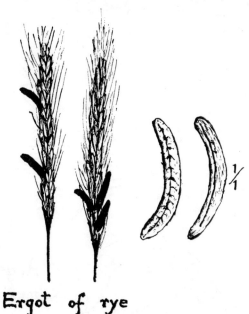

Ergot of rye

of poisoning have been reported as recently as 1951 in France from contamination of rye bread with fungus (Gabbai *et al.*, 1951). It has occurred also from contamination of other grain and grain products (Review, 1962). A recent review is given by Wilson (1966). Gangrene of the limbs and other parts, and convulsive disorders are two types of poisoning that have been described. Intense pheripheral vascoconstriction produced by certain alkaloids of ergot, for example ergotamine, may produce gangrene (St. Anthony's fire; ignis St. Antonii). Pregnant women abort or may die from the oxytocic activity of some of the alkaloids. Nausea, vomiting, tremors, excitement, confusion and convulsions may arise from central stimulation and vascular spasm. Anginal pain may be induced in subjects with coronary insufficiency.

Six pairs of ergot alkaloids are known. They are indicated in the following table where the more physiologically active member of each pair is given first. These alkaloids are derivatives of lysergic acid. Ergot also contains other constituents such as the amines histamine and tyramine, amino acids, acetylcholine and sterols such as ergosterol and fungisterol.

1. Ergometrine group	Ergometrine Ergometrinine	$C_{19}H_{23}O_2N_3$
2. Ergotamine group	Ergotamine Ergotaminine	$C_{33}H_{35}O_5N_5$
	Ergosine Ergosinine	$C_{30}H_{37}O_5N_5$
3. Ergotoxine group	Ergocristine Ergocristinine	$C_{35}H_{39}O_5N_5$
	Ergocryptine Ergocryptinine	$C_{32}H_{41}O_5N_5$
	Ergocornine Ergocorninine	$C_{31}H_{39}O_5N_5$

Ergotamine, R=$-CH_3$, R'=$-CH_2-$⬡

THE *Senecio* ALKALOIDS. These alkaloids have been a cause of bread poisoning in South Africa (Sapeika, 1952; Watt and Breyer-Brandwyk, 1962). *Senecio* species have been harvested with the corn and through improper winnowing have then caused liver damage and death when contaminated bread was eaten. Due to special measures and legislation this type of poisoning no longer occurs. These plants have caused poisoning in many countries, especially in certain animals. Much chemical and experimental investigation has been performed; many of the alkaloids have been shown to be hepatotoxic and some have been found to be carcinogenic in laboratory animals.

The genus *Senecio* belongs to the family compositae, and about two thousand varieties are found all over the world. A list of the more important species and details about them is given by Steyn (1933), Watt and Breyer-Brandwyk (1962), the Dispensatory of the United States (1955), and Warren (1955; 1966). The plants are rich in alkaloids. Many have been studied because of their toxic action on the liver in horses, cattle, goats, swine, man and laboratory animals. Many of the alkaloids belong to the pyrrolizidine group and similar alkaloids are found in the genera *Heliotropium* and *Trichodesma* (Boraginaceae), in several species of *Crotalaria* (Leguminosae), and in the families *Santalaceae* and *Gramineae* (Schoental, 1960; Warren, 1955, 1966).

Poisoning in man has occurred as stated above from the consumption of flour made from wheat contaminated with *Senecio* material. Desiccation has no effect on the activity of the alka-

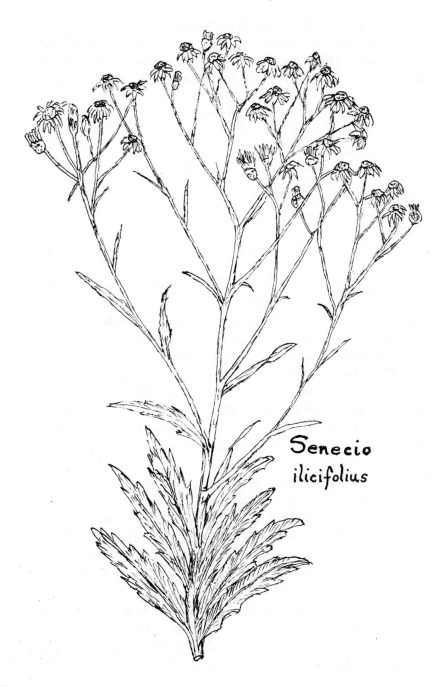

Senecio
ilicifolius

loids, nor are they destroyed by the process of baking. To prevent poisoning from this source it is laid down by law in South Africa in the Foods, Drugs and Disinfectants Act (No. 13 of 1929) regulation 12 (7) that "Every mill in which grain is milled for human

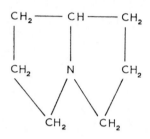

Pyrrolizidine

consumption shall be provided with efficient sieving and winnowing appliances so as completely to remove the seeds of *Senecio* (Springkaanbos) and every other poisonous or unwholesome seeds or matter. Any person selling any flour or meal containing such seeds or matter shall be guilty of an offence."

The clinical features of bread poisoning in South Africa have been reported by Willmot and Robertson (1920) and in greater detail by Selzer and Parker (1951), whose cases were regarded as examples of Chiari's syndrome, a condition characterized by the rapid development of ascites, hepatomegaly, abdominal pain, nausea and vomiting.

The use of certain *Senecio* plants in infusion as tea or for babies may cause "serous hepatosis" (Schoental, 1954). The possible significance of drinking "bush tea" in undernourished subjects in Jamaica as a cause of veno-occlusive disease in children and adolescents has been reported by Bras *et al.* (1954). The disease has been produced in animals poisoned with *Senecio* (Bras *et al.*, 1957; Hill, 1960).

Senecio alkaloids have been considered as a causal factor in the high incidence of primary carcinoma of the liver among the Bantu peoples. There have been many publications in relation to this subject, for example Cook *et al.* (1950), Schoental and Magee

(1959), Dybing and Erichsen (1959), Schoental (1963), Schoental *et al.* (1963). However, other contaminants of food have been suggested as responsible for hepatotoxic and carcinogenic effects in these people, for example the aflatoxins (Oettle, 1964; Butler and Barnes, 1966; Foy *et al.*, 1966).

There is a strong possibility that the hepatocarcinogenic *Senecio* alkaloids can act as alkylating agents (Culvenor *et al.*, 1962). This mode of action has been suggested also for toxic substances isolated from cycad seeds.

Chapter 3

FOODS OF ANIMAL ORIGIN

Animal protein is not essential for man, nevertheless the great majority of mankind has a natural appetite for meat. The presence of much fat in a meal has a delaying action on the emptying of the stomach, but both the protein and fat in meat are readily digested and absorbed.

Proteins and certain other items in the diet have a stimulating action on metabolism which is referred as the "specific dynamic effect"; carbohydrates and fat have a low specific dynamic effect. This stimulation was regarded as due to a pharmacodynamic effect, but in actual fact the heat is produced during chemical reactions such as the conversion of amino acids to urea, and glucose to glycogen.

Meat extracts such as Bovril, Oxo and other beef extracts supply only minor amounts of calories or protein and are not true foods. They act as stimulants of the appetite because of their content of the water-soluble constituents of muscle.

Pharmacological activity of food of land animal origin may be considered from two points of view. Firstly, the intrinsic composition of the food may temporarily or permanently make it unsuitable and even unsafe for certain individuals. Secondly, the presence of additives and especially of contaminants may render it potentially or actually harmful for all persons who consume such food.

MEAT

There is no evidence that protein of animal origin is essential for man, as amply demonstrated by many vegetarians who have lived full and active lives. The majority of mankind has a

84

natural appetite for meat, and the flesh of more than one hundred different species of animal is regularly eaten by man (Davidson and Passmore, 1966) as a source of protein of high biological value. Some flesh foods have been regarded as indigestible, but this probably in persons who are disposed to dyspepsia for any reason.

Protein in the diet, and other nitrogen-containing substances including a number of drugs, produces an abnormally increased concentration of ammonium ions in the blood in patients who have cirrhosis of the liver; also in those with gastrointestinal hemorrhage, surgical shunts, acute or chronic hepatic insufficiency, congestive heart failure, diabetic coma and chronic pulmonary emphysema. A variety of neurological symptoms may develop that progress to stupor, coma and death. The condition is referred to as hepatic coma or portacaval encephalopathy, and it has been known as meat poisoning and ptomaine poisoning. It may be controlled by feeding a protein-free diet and by other measures such as emptying the colon and the use of antibiotics to prevent intestinal putrefaction of food (Review, 1960).

In certain sensitive persons the ingestion of cooked crab meat has produced mild to severe anaphylactic shock. Pemmican, which is a prepared dried meat (buffalo; beef) used by the North American Indian and by explorers, may induce nausea, but this occurs mainly in persons already suffering from starvation (Review, 1961).

Meat extracts, for example Bovril, contain amines that can enter the blood stream when certain mono-amine oxidase inhibitors (MAOI) used as antidepressant drugs are being taken by depressed patients. A severe hypertensive reaction may arise, as may also occur when tyramine-containing cheese and certain other foods are ingested during administration of these drugs.

Sodium or potassium nitrate, or the nitrites, added to meat and meat products as preservatives have been the cause of many cases of poisoning (Steyn, 1960). Nitrates that may be present in vegetables and in water are considered in other sections of this book.

Sodium nicotinate or nicotinic acid used for the preservation of the red color in meat, to prevent its darkening, has caused nicotinic acid flushing and itching of the face and neck, nausea, abdominal cramps and sweating (Press and Yeager, 1962). Nicotinic acid in large doses may cause other toxic effects as described elsewhere in this book.

Meat grilled on skewers made from the wood of the ornamental shrub *Nerium oleander L.* (Ceylon rose) has caused death. All parts of this plant are poisonous due to presence of digitalis principles (Watt and Breyer-Brandwyk, 1962).

The disease known as cotyledonosis or krimpsiekte in South Africa has been recognized for many years. It has occurred in animals, especially goats and sheep, that have eaten certain plants of the genus Cotyledon containing neurotoxic and cardiotoxic principles (Sapeika, 1936; Watt and Breyer-Brandwyk, 1962). It has occurred in dogs that have eaten the meat, blood, or entrails of poisoned animals. Human beings, for example bushmen, have developed symptoms of krimpsiekte after eating raw or undercooked meat or the blood of a diseased animal. Properly cooked meat is safe. Meat from animals that have been hunted by primitive races and paralyzed by them with such drugs as curare alkaloids has not caused poisoning when eaten.

The widespread use of pesticides and the dissemination of radioactive materials over large areas has led to contamination of soil, water and plant and animal material. Meat and milk from cattle that have eaten this type of contaminated herbage present a danger to man that may become serious. Further details are given in the sections dealing with milk and pesticides.

CARCINOGENS IN MEAT. It has been demonstrated that broiled meat (steaks) and barbecued ribs, and smoked fish, contain complex polynuclear (polycyclic) hydrocarbons which include carcinogens; however, the latter are present in small quantities and are not regarded as dangerous to the consumer of such food (Review, 1965). Further details are given in a later section dealing with processing degradation products.

LIVER

Liver contains naturally a great number of substances, including a number of vitamins and anti-anemic (hematinic) principles. Preparations of liver and liver extracts contain anti-anemic principles, and at one time these were used in the treatment of pernicious anemia. They produce some beneficial effect when given by mouth together with a source of "intrinsic factor." Large quantities must be taken, and treatment may be unpleasant because of the bulk and objectionable taste of these products. Fresh beef liver contains approximately 1 μg of cobalamin per gm of wet weight. The naturally-occurring cobalamins are bound to protein, and there are foods other than liver which are richer in cobalamins.

Hydroxocobalamin and cyanocobalamin are nowadays used as pure substances in the treatment of pernicious anemia. Folic acid which is ubiquitous in nature especially in liver, yeast and fresh green vegetables is used in nutritional megaloblastic anemia and certain other megaloblastic anemia, but it should never be used in the treatment of pernicious anemia unless there is associated folate deficiency.

The livers of polar bears and certain other animals are extremely rich in vitamin A. Acute intoxication (hypervitaminosis A) has occurred in man, for example in Arctic explorers and in dogs, from the consumption of this material (Rodahl and Moore, 1943). The symptoms include drowsiness, headache, vomiting and extensive peeling of the skin. The livers of the Arctic fox, seal, whale and shark are also poisonous to man presumably because of the high content of vitamin A. Hypervitaminosis A is also considered in more detail in another section of this book. The amount of vitamin A present in liver and certain other foods rich in this vitamin is indicated in the following table. Details about the constituents of these and many other foods are given, for example, in *Documenta Geigy-Scientific Tables* (1962) and Hawk (1965).

VITAMIN A (IU PER 100 GM WEIGHT, FRESH)

Cod-liver oil	200,000
Halibut-liver oil	4-6 million (+)
Shark-liver oil	3 million (+)
Polar bear liver	1.8 million
Seal liver	1.3 million
Tunny (tuna)	0.8-8 million
Tunny (tinned)	70-200
Sardines	4,800-54,000
Sardines (tinned)	136-290
Herring	9,000
Liver (sheep and ox)	4,000-45,000
Butter	2,400-4,000

The livers of several species of tropical sharks may cause severe poisoning with gastrointestinal and neurological symptoms. Recovery may take several days or weeks. The nature of the poison is unknown. It is not destroyed by heat and gastric juice (Halstead, 1964).

Chicken livers eaten by patients taking mono-amine oxidase inhibitors as antidepressants may evoke hypertension with central nervous system and circulatory effects, as may occur when foods such as Bovril, cheese, yeast extract, alcoholic beverages, pickled herring and broad beans are taken with these drugs.

MILK

The uses and limitations of cow's milk as a food and as a source of certain elements, for example to provide calcium in rachitic infants and children and to provide protein in kwashiorkor, will not be considered here. Milk in any form in sufficiently large quantity tends to lessen putrefaction in the intestine. Certain special preparations are available for this purpose.

Milk soured by the introduction of cultures of lactic-acid-producing organisms such as *L. acidophilus* or *L. bulgaricus* is sometimes beneficial especially in children, for example in summer diarrhea, in enteritis and colitis. Chronic constipation in adults may also be corrected by this treatment.

Yogurt (yoghurt; yoghourt) is used both as a food and a therapeutic agent. It is a product of pasteurized milk inoculated with *L. bulgaricus* and *Strept. thermophilus*. It changes the intestinal flora and thus removes putrefaction and other organisms, i.e., it produces the same effect as acidophilus milk.

Milk as an Antacid

Milk has abundantly been used in the management of gastric and duodenal ulcer. However, as far as gastric acidity is concerned, it has been shown that hourly drinks of milk and cream are less effective than a light diet in buffering the acidity of the gastric contents of patients with duodenal ulcer (Bingle and Lennard-Jones, 1960; Lennard-Jones 1966). Milk rapidly leaves the stomach and cannot contribute to any prolonged neutralization of acid-pepsin secretion in the stomach. Also, while milk administered by continuous intragastric drip may afford quick relief from severe and persistent pain, it does not hasten the healing of the ulcer (Doll *et al.*, 1956; Doll, 1964). Traditional ulcer diets also no more effectively relieve pain or hasten healing of gastric or duodenal ulcers than freely chosen diets that do not contain foods (fried foods) that cause pain (Leading Article, 1965).

Milk ingested for months in large doses with much soluble absorbable alkali has caused hypercalcemia, metastatic calcification in the arteries and kidneys (nephrocalcinosis) and other features, a condition known as Burnett's syndrome. An interesting feature in late cases is corneal calcification recognized at first with the slit lamp, and later when there is complaint of poor vision, the calcification can be recognized by the naked eye (Locket, 1957). Excessive milk feeding in infants and children has caused iron-deficiency anemia, and milk-puree diets can in adults lead to ascorbic acid and iron deficiency, constipation, or diarrhea and flatus.

Milk as an Antidote

Milk is a useful household antidote and demulcent, together with other measures, for certain poisons that have been ingested. Thus milk and raw egg white because of their protein content may be used to precipitate metals such as arsenic, lead, mercury and other heavy metals. Milk is also used to counteract the action of ingested sulphuric, nitric, or hydrochloric acids; in oxalic acid poisoning it is given immediately by mouth to precipitate the oxalate as the insoluble calcium salt. It is also given when the salts of hypochlorous acid (used as bleaching agents) have been swallowed. Most foods in the stomach tend to reduce the effects of ingested alcohol, but milk is especially efficacious in inhibiting the absorption of alcohol (Miller *et al.*, 1966).

Harmful Substances in Milk

Many substances have been demonstrated to be present in cow's milk and in human milk (Sapeika, 1959; Sisodia and Stowe, 1964; Knowles, 1965; Robson *et al.*, 1965; *Extra Pharmacopoeia*, 1967). Irradiation of dairy products containing fat may cause disagreeable oxidation flavors to develop (Bongirwar and Kumta, 1967).

Cow's milk may contain pesticides (Review, 1960; Annotation, 1965; Leading Article, 1965), and pesticide residues may be found in human milk (Egan *et al.*, 1965). Antibiotics, radionuclides, fungal toxins and active principles from certain plants may also be present, as indicated below.

ANTIBIOTICS may be present in milk. Penicillin in milk has caused skin and allergic reactions in persons sensitive to this antibiotic (Meyler, 1966). Streptomycin and possibly chloramphenicol may also be incriminated in this respect (*WHO techn. Rep. No.* 260, 1963). Antibiotic contamination of cow's milk resulting from the treatment of the animals for mastitis is potentially harmful in two respects: (a) The antibiotic may cause adverse reactions in certain persons receiving such milk, (b) It may inhibit the normal growth of the starter cultures used in the manufacture of cheese and cultured milk products.

RADIONUCLIDES. There is much literature on the subject of radionuclides in cow's milk. The following references may be consulted: Sapeika (1959), Anderson *et al.* (1960), Madshus and Baarli (1960), McNeil and Trojan (1960), Rundo (1960), Annotation (1960), Any Questions (1961), Report (1961), Review (1961), Carr and Mercer (1962), Knapp (1964), Comar (1966), Hvinden and Lillegraven (1966), Bird (1966), Woodwell (1967). Further details are given in the section dealing with food contaminants.

PLANT SUBSTANCES. Cow's milk may taste of onions or smell of wild garlic or cod-liver oil when these substances have been in-

gested by the animal.   Death has occurred in an infant who drank
the milk of a cow that had eaten the foliage of *Nerium oleander L.*
(Watt and Breyer-Brandwyk, 1962) .

Milk sickness (trembles; alkali disease) is a disorder of cattle
caused by eating white snake-root *(Eupatorium urticaefolium*
Reich.) or rayless goldenrod (jimmy weed) *(Aplopappus hetero-
phyllus* [A. Gray] Blake) ; the plants occur in Texas, New Mexico

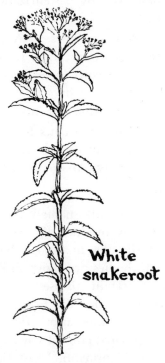

White
snakeroot

and Arizona.   The poison in the milk (or meat) of animals has
also caused illness in man, as originally discovered by Dr. Anna
Pierce Hobbs (Sniveley, 1966).   Several members of the Lincoln
family including the mother of Abraham Lincoln and many early
settlers in the United States died of this "milk sickness" (Locket,
1957).   Anorexia, nausea, severe vomiting, abdominal pain, constipation, prostration, jaundice from liver damage, oliguria and
anuria from kidney damage, and convulsions may occur (Arena,
1963).   There is also hypoglycemia, ketosis and lipemia.   The

cheeks, lips and tongue are characteristically red. Death has usually occurred in one or two weeks, often preceded by convulsions and prolonged coma. In those who recovered from poisoning there was weakness persisting for months. The leaves and stem of the plants mentioned contain tremetol, a toxic unsaturated alcohol $C_{16}H_{22}O_3$ which in consistency and odor resembles turpentine; it inhibits mobilization of glucose from liver glycogen. The poison is not destroyed by pasteurization of contaminated milk or milk products.

GOITROGENIC SUBSTANCES. These may be present in milk. They are found in cabbage (*q.v.*), kale, turnips, rape seeds and certain other plants. When cows ingest such fodder, their milk contains goitrogens (such as goitrin) which have been suspected as the cause of goiters in Tasmania and Australia (Clements, 1960).

FUNGAL TOXINS. Milk from cows fed very toxic aflatoxin-containing groundnut meal can induce liver lesions in ducklings (de Jongh *et al.*, 1964, see also Aflatoxins).

Antibody Production

The proteins of cow's milk, namely bovine serum albumin and alph-lactalbumin, may produce abnormally high concentrations of circulating antibodies in human blood (maternal and cord blood). Such antibodies are more likely to be present in persons suffering from certain diseases of the alimentary canal such as ulcerative colitis, celiac disease and idiopathic steatorrhea (Wright *et al.*, 1962; Annotation, 1964). The circulating antibody has not been equated clinically with sensitivity reactions to milk (Review, 1965; Mansmann, 1966).

Antibodies in human colostrum and mature milk apparently do not survive digestion in significant quantities. Sensitivity to cow's milk has been the subject of a report from the Council on Foods and Nutrition (Heiner *et al.*, 1964).

Synthetic Milk and Baby Feeding Formulae

The use of cow's milk for infant feeding has led to the recognition of allergies to the milk, and to other forms of intolerance. In the United States, the Committee on Nutrition (1963) has examined the nutritional adequacy of formulae used as substitutes for cow's milk. The main alternative sources of protein considered were milks from other animals, soya preparations, and hydrolyzed casein.

Synthetic foods given to infants cause deficiency states. Low-calcium milk and low-sodium milk have been associated with similar symptoms. During the preparation of these synthetic milks many nutrients are washed out. Although minerals and vitamins are restored, these may be insufficient (Mann *et al.*, 1965). Care is required in using these foods, for example in the treatment of phenylketonuria and galactosemia. The disease under treatment with synthetic food is not necessarily the cause of the failure of the infant to thrive.

The accidental use of sodium nitrite (anti-rust tablets) in the preparation of feeds for babies has caused poisoning and deaths from methemoglobinemia. The use of certain types of drinking water (well water, bore-hole water), containing nitrates has also caused such poisoning (Locket, 1957; Steyn, 1960; Knotek and Schmidt, 1964). The low acidity of the gastric contents of infants is believed to permit the growth of flora which reduces nitrate to nitrite, which then converts the hemoglobin to methemoglobin.

Boric acid has also caused poisoning when accidentally included in feeding formulae. Babies have been given dettol (a disinfectant) and water in mistake for milk with fatal results.

CHEESE

Various cheeses whether natural or aged, for example cheddar, Camembert and Stilton, have been found to contain tyramine (Asatoor *et al.*, 1963; Horwitz *et al.*, 1964; Blackwell and Mabbitt, 1965). There may be enough amine present to produce a marked rise in blood pressure and other cardiovascuar changes in patients receiving antidepressant drugs that are mono-amine oxidase inhibitors, for example tranylcypromine, phenelzine and nialamide. These drugs inhibit the enzyme in the intestine and the liver (Thomas, 1963; Annotation, 1964). Sudden severe headache in the occiput, characteristically of a throbbing nature and lasting for twenty minutes to several hours, is associated with the marked rise in blood pressure. Death may occur from intracranial hemorrhage. An attack has followed the ingestion of as little as one ounce (28.5 gm) of cheddar cheese. Many of the attacks have occurred between half an hour and two hours after the patient had eaten the cheese (Asatoor *et al.*, 1963). The tyramine present in the cheese is presumed to escape oxidative deamination that would normally occur in the liver. It enters the general circulation, releases noradrenaline from local stores in nerve endings and also prolongs the action of noradrenaline on adrenergic receptors. Other foods known to produce these hypertensive crises in the presence of the mono-amine oxidase inhibitors are Marmite, Bovril, broad beans, pickled herring, chicken liver and certain wines, for example Chianti. It is possible that in certain susceptible individuals attacks of migraine (sick headache) are induced by tyramine and other amines present in cheese, milk dairy products and certain other foods such as beans, fish, chocolate and alcohol (Hannington, 1967).

Molds may be present in cheese. They may have been put there purposely in the course of manufacture, or the cheese may be contaminated adventitiously with fungal spores subsequent to its manufacture. There are very many types of mold, and many produce toxic substances from which the danger cannot on present knowledge be completely excluded. Radionuclides may be present in cheese (Review, 1961).

EGGS

Egg yolk consists of about 50 per cent water and 20 per cent oil emulsified by about 7 per cent lecithin (ovolecithin) and 15 per cent phosphoprotein vitellin. Lecithins occur in all animal and vegetable cells and vary in composition; egg lecithin differs from vegetable lecithin in that it contains cholesterol and a higher percentage of phosphorus.

Eggs are a common allergen in children and adults (Mansmann, 1966); they may be a cause of urticaria and asthma. In such individuals eggs and foods containing them, for example biscuits and cakes, must be excluded from the diet.

Egg yolks and animal fat contain most of the dietary cholesterol; related sterols occur in plants, but these are not absorbed from the gastrointestinal tract. The relation of dietary factors to the blood lipids are considered below.

Raw egg white inactivates the vitamin-B complex factor known as biotin; the binding factor (antivitamin) in the egg white is a protein, avidin. Egg white also contains ovomucoids (antienzymes) that inhibit trypsin (Ambrose, 1966).

Antibiotics may be given in therapeutic amounts to poultry, but the eggs from such poultry should not be sold for human consumption (Report of Expert Committee on the Public Health Aspects of Food and Feedstuffs, *WHO techn. Rep. Ser. No.* 260 1963).

Pesticides which are increasingly being used in agriculture and horticulture have been reported to be present in the eggs of a number of species of birds (Dunachie and Fletcher, 1966). Eggs may show radioactivity (Comar, 1966).

DIETARY FACTORS AND BLOOD LIPIDS

Atherosclerosis is a disorder in which the intima of certain arteries show a deposition of lipid that leads to narrowing of the vessels and consequent reduction in blood supply. Most patients also have high serum lipids such as cholesterol, fatty acids, lipoproteins and phospholipids. The importance of dietary habits (Reviews 1960, 1964, 1965, 1966) relating to the intake of certain fats, sugars and alcohol as etiological factors are considered in other sections of this book. The following agents have been used in attempts to produce improvement in this condition and to prevent complications arising from the disorder.

Polyunsaturated fatty acids have been used. They occur in large amounts in the oils and fats of certain seeds and in some animal fats such as certain marine animal oils. Oleic, linoleic and linolenic acids are present in linseed, peanut and cottonseed oils, and arachidonic acid is of fish and animal origin.

UNSATURATED FATTY ACIDS IN FOODS

Oleic	$C_{17}H_{33}COOH$	(1)	In all fats and oils
Linoleic	$C_{17}H_{31}COOH$	(2)	Mostly in vegetable oils (e.g., sunflower, soybean, safflower)
Linolenic	$C_{17}H_{29}COOH$	(3)	Mainly in linseed oil
Arachidonic	$C_{19}H_{31}COOH$	(4)	In fish oils and animal fats

(The number in brackets indicates the number of double bonds; those with more than one double bond are polyunsaturated).

These acids and the oils containing them have been added to the diet in attempts to lower blood cholesterol levels in patients who have hypercholesterolemia. However, a relationship between this condition and atherosclerosis has not yet been proved, and the clinical value of such treatment has not yet been established in atherosclerosis or coronary artery disease. The value of unsaturated fatty acids as a dietary addition or substitute has been much discussed, for example, Brock (1961), *Todays Drugs* (1964). The possibility of ill effects from the use of highly unsaturated fats to lower serum cholesterol has to be considered; excessive consumption of unsaturated fats may be a causal factor of carcinoma of the stomach amongst the Japanese and Swedes (Harman, 1957). The fatty acids from certain liquid vegetable oils for example linolenic acid, and those from marine oils, may act by aiding the transport and elimination of cholesterol.

Sitosterols are plant sterols closely related to cholesterol; sitosterol has the same structure as cholesterol except for an ethyl group attached to carbon 24 (Reviews, 1962; 1964). They have been shown to lower raised serum cholesterol levels and β-lipoprotein levels in one to three weeks. However, large doses are required, 10 to 25 gm daily in divided doses given before meals. They produce toxic effects including anorexia, diarrhea and cramps. These plant sterols appear to prevent cholesterol absorption in the intestine by competing for sites of esterification. Increased excretion of steroids in the feces has been demonstrated.

Other substances that have been used include drugs such as clofibrate (Atromid-S®) which is a branched-chain fatty acid ester, a substituted isobutyric acid, also thyroxine, and nicotinic acid in large doses. Details with regard to drugs that have been used to lower the serum cholesterol in the prevention and treatment of atherosclerosis may be found elsewhere, for example Review (1964), and in the textbooks of Drill (1965), and Goodman and Gilman (1965).

Nicotinic acid has been used with some success by some investigators for hypercholesterolemia, but its value is not established. Large pharmacological doses of this vitamin must be given, 3 to 6 gm daily in divided doses. Nicotinamide has none of the potency of nicotinic acid as a hypocholesterolemic agent. Nicotinic acid produces a loss of cholesterol from β-lipoprotein, but α-lipoprotein cholesterol remains unchanged or becomes somewhat elevated. In some cases a fall in serum triglyceride level also occurs. The toxic effects produced by nicotinic acid are mainly itching and flushing which may persist for several weeks. In some patients the large doses given for long periods have produced liver damage and diabetes mellitus (Reviews, 1961, 1962, 1964; Molnar *et al.*, 1964; Meyler, 1966).

As a matter of interest it may be added that vanadium, which is widely distributed in nature—for instance in various fruits, vegetables and plants and in various marine organisms, can profoundly influence cholesterol metabolism. There is evidence that when it is included in the diet (or through occupational exposure) it can lower serum cholesterol and tissue cholesterol stores in man by inhibiting cholesterol synthesis (Review 1960). The significance of this is discussed by Hudson (1964).

In conclusion it may be stated that it remains to be proved that dietary measures will prevent or retard the development of atherosclerosis in man, although there would appear to be a close association between the disease and a high plasma cholesterol determined by the quantity and quality of the dietary fat (Brock, 1961; Davidson and Passmore, 1966). There is evidence that dietary regulation of serum cholesterol can diminish the risk of coronary heart disease (Review, 1967). The view put forward by Cleave and Campbell (1966) and by other workers, that sugar and white flour consumed in large quantity may be responsible for a number of disorders including ischemic heart disease has been referred to in another section (see Sweetening agents).

Representative values of the total fat and cholesterol content (gm per 100 gm edible uncooked food) of some foods are given in the table below. The dash (—) indicates that no data are available.

	Fat	Cholesterol
Almond (dried)	54.1	0.05
Bacon	55-85	—
Brazil nuts	65.9	—
Butter	81	0.28
Cashew nuts (roasted)	48.2	—
Cheese (cottage)	0.5	—
Other cheese	25-36	0.13-0.19
Cocoa	18.8	—
Cod-liver Oil	100	0.85
Egg yolk (raw)	31.9	1.3
Fish roes	2	0.3
Ham	22-33	—
Liver (calf)	4.9	0.36
Mayonnaise	78	—
Milk	3.6	0.01
Olive Oil	100	—
Peanuts (roasted)	46.1	—
Peanut butter	47.8	—
Pecans (raw)	73	—
Sweetbread	15	2.5

Further details with regard to the above foods and other foods are available in *Documenta Geigy-Scientific Tables* (1962) and Hawk (1965).

Dietary cholesterol and other fats have been investigated as possibly favoring the growth of certain malignant tumors in laboratory animals. Also, studies in man have indicated positive correlations between the consumption of fat and the occurrence of certain neoplasms (Review, 1967). Much more evidence from controlled clinical and laboratory studies will be needed before such correlations as have been described can be accepted.

Chapter 4

FOOD OF MARINE ANIMAL ORIGIN

Consideration is given in this chapter to marine animals which regularly produce or which temporarily contain active principles that may cause poisoning when they are ingested by man. Descriptions and details of many aspects relating to poisonous and venomous marine animals of the world have recently been published in the fascinating encyclopedic volume of Halstead (1965), also in the comprehensive reviews by Halstead (1964) and Russell (1965), in the biological data given by Altman and Dittmer (1964), and in a review of seafood toxins by Wills (1966). Some details and illustrations of a number of poisonous fish are given by Dewberry (1959) and by Dreisbach (1966).

SHELLFISH POISONING

Mussels may occasionally cause illness, and even death. Three types of poisoning are recognized: (a) erythematous (allergic) type in which symptoms occur from hypersensitivity to the shellfish; (b) gastrointestinal or choleratic (bacterial) type in which poisoning results from pathogenic organisms, for example typhoid bacilli present in mussels collected from sewage-contamined beds; (c) paralytic type, most dangerous, which is due to a potent paralytic poison. This type has been recognized at least since 1793 (Meyer *et al.,* 1928). It is this form of poisoning that is considered here, caused by the shellfish toxin also known as clam toxin, mussel toxin and saxitoxin (from its presence in the Alaskan butterclam *Saxidomus giganteus*).

Paralytic shellfish poisoning occurs when certain molluscs (mussels, clams, scallops) that have ingested toxic dinoflagellates are subsequently eaten by man.   Under certain conditions "blooms" of toxic protistan dinoflagellates that are taken up by molluscs may cause the phenomenon known as red water or red tide, visible in the daytime and luminescent at night; this heralds an outbreak of shellfish poisoning.

Toxic shellfish have been found sporadically in many parts of the world, but some areas are especially affected such as the Pacific coast of North America, the Bay of Fundy, the North Sea and the English Channel.   Certain coastal regions of South Africa, for example the False Bay and St. Helena Bay areas have been affected in recent years.

On the Canadian Atlantic Coast the red or horse mussel and the blue, black or common mussel, and to a lesser extent also the bar clam, razor clam or razor fish, the smooth or sea scallop, and the soft shell clam have on occasion been found to contain the poisonous principle.

In American waters the danger of poisoning occurs especially during the summer months (May to September).   In certain areas the possibility of toxicity of shellfish is regularly checked by assay procedures conducted by the Department of Fisheries.

The molluscan species that have been reported to transvect dinoflagellate poison are listed by Halstead (1965) and Russell (1965), and much other information is also provided by these authors.   A valuable review of the pharmacology and other aspects of the toxin has been published by Kao (1966).

Paralytic shellfish poisoning may also be caused by at least one species of echinoderm and one arthropod.   The poison has also been found in the proventriculus and in the digestive gland of the rock lobster (crawfish (*Jasus lalandii*) collected at Lambert's Bay at the time of "red water" and demonstrable poisonous mussels, December 1966 (Sapeika; personal observation).

Poisonous mussels are indistinguishable from normal ones. They are themselves unaffected by the toxin which can only be detected by animal toxicity tests, for example the Sommer-Meyer test, which is very useful; but an easy, reliable quantitative chemical test for the poison is desirable.

The usual methods of cooking do not reliably remove the poison, and even the addition of sodium bicarbonate and prolonged cooking will not ensure removal of all the poison. The digestive glands (hepatopancreas) and gills of black mussels (*Mytilus*) and broth in which the shellfish have been cooked should be discarded; the white meat of shellfish such as in white mussels (*Donax serra*) is generally harmless, but poison may diffuse into it from the digestive gland during preparatory soaking and eventual cooking of the mussels (Sapeika, 1958).

The clinical features of poisoning have been described by many authors. These are given in some detail by Halstead (1965), who also provides lists of the reported outbreaks and the mortality rates that have been recorded. Cases of poisoning in South Africa have been reported by Sapeika (1958). The pathognomonic symptoms arise within thirty minutes and include a tingling or burning sensation on the lips, gums, tongue and face, spreading to other parts of the body; this paresthesia changes to numbness. In severe cases ataxia and interference with speech and swallowing occur. Most patients remain calm and conscious throughout their episode. Twitchings and convulsions are rare. In the terminal stages there is motor weakness, and paralysis becomes progressively more severe. Death occurs from respiratory paralysis, usually within twelve hours. If the patient survives the first twelve hours the prognosis is good. The pathological findings in deaths from paralytic shellfish poisoning are not characteristic nor of great significance. Treatment is symptomatic as there is no specific antidote; artificial respiration has been suggested from experimental studies (Sapeika, 1953; Murtha, 1960). Digitalis and alcohol are not recommended.

Paralytic shellfish poison is one of the most lethal biological substances known. One mussel, clam, or oyster may contain a fatal dose of poison. Man is very sensitive to it; the minimal lethal oral dose of purified toxin may be between 1 to 4 mg (Tennant *et al.*, 1955; Kao, 1966). The chemical structure of this poison is one of the most complex in the field of natural products and still remains to be elucidated. The empirical formula for the hydrochloride has been given as $C_{10}H_{17}N_7O_4.2HCl$ and the molecular weight 372 (Schantz, 1960) , but there is doubt about this; the formula may more correctly be $C_{10}H_{15}N_7O_4$ (Kao, 1966) . It does not appear to be a quarternary ammonium compound, nor an inhibitor of cholinesterase. A review of this chemistry is presented by D. A. Courville in Halstead (1965) , and by Kao (1966) .

The pharmacological effects of paralytic shellfish poison have been described by Prinzmetal et al. (1932) , Kellaway (1935 a.b) , Sapeika (1953) , Fingerman *et al.* (1953) , Murtha (1960) , and reviewed by Halstead (1965) , Russell (1965) , and Kao (1966) . The principal actions are on the nervous system especially the peripheral nervous system (neuromuscular junction, cutaneous tactile endings and muscle spindles) , and there is direct depression of the heart. Evans (1965) found that the toxin appears to act directly on skeletal muscle including the diaphragm and produces paralysis by abolishing muscle action potential. Kao *et al.* (1967) have reported from observations on cross-experiments on cats and dogs that the hypotension and respiratory depression are due to paralysis of peripheral nerves and muscles and not to direct actions on medullary and respiratory centers.

SPONGES

There is no detailed knowledge of human intoxication from the ingestion of sponges.

SEA ANEMONES

Only certain species are eaten and they are generally cooked. Some have been found to be poisonous when eaten raw. Gastrointestinal symptoms, cyanosis, prostration and prolonged shock may occur, and finally death associated with pulmonary edema. There is no known antidote.

STARFISHES

The slime of certain species of starfish may cause swelling of the lips or skin if it touches them. There is otherwise no information about symptoms in man caused by the ingestion of poisonous starfishes. Death has been produced in cats that ate such material; ataxia and convulsions may first occur.

SEA URCHINS

Ingestion of the ovaries of certain species may cause gastro-intestinal symptoms and possibly migrainelike attacks in certain susceptible persons. This has occurred off the coast of Japan, Barbados and the other West Indies. Studies on the mode of action of sea urchin toxin have been reported by Feigen *et al.* (1966).

SEA CUCUMBERS

The sea cucumber is a holotharian worm regarded as a delicacy by the Chinese. Ingestion of poison of these animals may cause nausea and vomiting. Death rarely occurs.

WHELKS (SNAILS AND SLUGS)

Headache, dizziness, urticaria, visual disturbances and gastro-intestinal upset are the main symptoms arising from consumption of marine gastropods such as *Neptuna arthritica,* which are widely distributed in the north seas of Japan. Some species contain the poison tetramine in their salivary glands, and removal of the gland therefore can protect consumers from food poisoning. Tetramine is an autonomic ganglion blocking agent which resembles tetrodontoxin toxicologically but is chemically different (Asano and Itoh, 1960). A similar active principle has been found in other gastropod species, for example *Neptuna antiqua* (almond or red whelk, barnagh) the eating of which does not seem to have been reported as causing poisoning (Fänge, 1960).

ABALONE

Only the muscular foot known as abalone steak should be eaten as the viscera may produce burning, itching, redness, edema and even ulceration of the skin of those parts of the body exposed to sunlight. This is a rare phenomenon in man in which photo-sensitization is induced by a food of animal origin.

CRUSTACEANS

Bacterial infections and allergic reactions have frequently resulted from the ingestion of marine crustaceans. Poisoning may be produced by the Asiatic horseshoe crab especially during the reproductive season of the year; gastrointestinal, sensory and motor symptoms occur, and death may result within sixteen hours. Sand crabs may become poisonous occasionally from feeding on the unicellular protistan, *Gonyaulax*. Rock lobsters (*Jasus lalandii*) have been found to have paralytic shellfish poison in their digestive glands at a time when black and white mussels were also demonstrably poisonous (Sapeika; personal observation).

POISONOUS FISHES

Approximately five hundred species of marine fishes are known to be toxic, and may be poisonous when eaten by man. Some are poisonous at all times, others only at certain periods or only in certain areas.

a. One type of fish poisoning (ichthyosarcotoxism) (ciguatera) (gymnothorax poisoning) follows the ingestion of fish ordinarily considered edible. They contain a heat-stable poison within their muscles, viscera, or skin, that produces gastrointestinal symptoms including cramps, and neurological manifestations that may resemble those of paralytic shellfish poisoning. The onset of symptoms is within thirty-six hours, with tingling sensations about the lips, tongue, throat and then numbness. Dryness of the mouth, nausea, vomiting and abdominal cramps are common features. Headache, dizziness, itching, restlessness, blurring of vision, ataxia and convulsions may occur. Deaths have been reported. Barracudas, sea bass, mackerel, surgeon fish, snapper, jacks, perch and certain other fish may cause this type of poisoning. The species of fish and their distribution as well as references to publications on the chemisttry and toxicology are given by Altman and Dittmer (1964) and Wills (1966). Case reports, and a review of the literature, are presented by Moffie and Haneveld (1964).

Most dangerous is tetraodon poisoning following the ingestion of the flesh, or the liver, ovaries and testes, of certain puffers or pufferlike fishes, known as globe fishes, balloon fishes, blowfishes, blaasops and toadfishes. The species of fish and their distribution, and references to publications on the chemistry and toxicity of the poison, are given by Altman and Dittmer (1964).

The chemistry and pharmacology of tetraodontoxin and much other detail including a list of the animals containing this toxin and related substances are considered by Kao (1966), Fuhrman (1967), and Kao *et al.* (1967).

Many persons die each year from this poisoning in Japan, where the tetraodon fishes are well known for their "fugu poison"; the poison has also been used particularly in Japan for suicidal and homicidal purposes. Poisoning and death from eating globe fish has occurred on the West Coast of Africa, the Cape, Japan, Australia, California, the East Indies and Brazil.

Tetraodontoxin is a neurotoxin. It produces rapid onset, within ten to fifty minutes, of weakness, dizziness, pallor, paraesthesiae (tingling and numbness) in the lips, mouth and tongue, with salivation, nausea, vomiting and dysphagia. Paraesthesiae and paresis occur also in different parts of the body; respiratory distress, cyanosis, convulsions and coma may occur, and death in six to twenty-four hours in about 50 per cent of cases. The toxin affects nerve, muscle and neuromuscular transmission directly. It also affects the contractile force of the heart. It causes respiratory failure by a peripheral action. The poison is not destroyed by ordinary cooking; it will withstand boiling for four to six hours. It is soluble. The empirical formula is $C_{11}H_{17}N_3O_8$. It is of interest that an extraordinary potent non-protein neurotoxin called tarichotoxin that has been isolated from the eggs of various species of western (California) American newts of the genus Taricha is identical with tetraodontoxin (Mosher *et al.*, 1964; Fuhrman, 1967).

Tunas and bonitos when inadequately preserved occasionally produce gastrointestinal symptoms, flushing of the face, headache, burning of the throat and thirst, and generalized urticaria, i.e., a syndrome resembling histamine poisoning. Antihistamines certainly alleviate the reaction. The livers of several species of tropical sharks have caused severe poisoning and even death. Hypervitaminosis A has been suggested as responsible for the poisoning.

"Hallucinatory fish poisoning" characterized by light-headedness, weakness, dizziness, incoordination, hallucinations and depression, with lack of gastrointestinal symptoms has occurred following the ingestion of certain mullet and "goatfish" from Hawaii areas, also possibly from Norfolk Island in the South Pacific and in the waters of South Africa. Few cases are serious, but paresthesiae, paralysis and dyspnea may occur.

b. Fresh-water fishes and a few marine species may cause another type of poisoning (ichthyotoxic) following ingestion of the roe, or the gonads and roe. Gastrointestinal and other symptoms, and in severe cases respiratory distress, convulsions and coma may occur. Usually there is complete recovery within a few days.

c. Many species of fishes and eels have been found to contain a toxic substance in their blood (ichthyohemotoxic fishes). Poisoning from this source is very rare.

d. Poisoning from fish may sometimes produce allergic crises precipitated by a specific protein sensitivity.

e. Certain types of raw fish, but not the boiled fish, contain a substance which interferes with the absorption of iron in mink kits (Havre *et al.*, 1967). A type of hypochromic and microcytic anemia develops which induces achromotrichia and cotton fur. There appears to be a genetic factor involved in this susceptibility to anemia since not all kits in a litter are affected by raw fish in their food ration (Mickelsen and Yong, 1966).

TURTLE

The ingestion of the flesh of certain species of turtle, for example the green sea turtle, leatherneck sea turtle, and hawksbill sea turtle, may rarely cause poisoning. The symptoms occur within one to twenty-four hours and include nausea, vomiting, salivation, abdominal cramps, diarrhea, dysphagia and paraesthesiae. Coma and deaths have also been reported (Altman and Dittmer, 1964).

CONTAMINANTS IN FOODS OF MARINE ANIMAL ORIGIN

The presence of contaminants such as pesticides and radionuclides in a great variety of foods of plant and animal origin is considered in other sections of this book (see Food Contaminants). Recent reports reveal that certain fish especially saury, salmon and tuna contain measurable amounts of iron—55, half-life 2.94 years (Review, 1967).

Pickled herrings may contain tyramine and are therefore potentially dangerous for patients taking antidepressants of the mono-amine oxidase inhibitor type (Nuessle *et al.*, 1965). Other foods containing amines are also harmful in this respect, for example cheese, Marmite, broad beans, chicken liver and certain wines. Samples of herring meal preserved with sodium nitrite may contain dimethylnitrosamine which is hepatotoxic (Saksaug *et al.*, 1966).

FISH-LIVER OILS

Fish-liver oils, and certain other animal products, are among the best sources of vitamin A. The provitamin occurs most abundantly in carrots and other yellow vegetables and in many green vegetables. The fish-liver oils are the best source of vitamin D; the flesh of oily fish is also an excellent source.

Cod-liver oil is a valuable source of vitamins A and D and of readily digestible fat. It also contains several unsaturated fatty acids which are essential food factors. It has long been used as a dietary supplement for infants and children who are undernourished or have rickets. It is commonly used in animal nutrition. Excessive doses may lower the fat content of milk, cause gastrointestinal disturbances, and induce vitamin E deficiency. It may taint the flesh of bacon or pork pigs.

Halibut-liver oil usually has a higher proportion of vitamin A to vitamin D than cod-liver oil; the composition of the fatty acids is similar to that in cod-liver oil, but the proportion of unsaturated fatty acids is lower. Gross overdosage can lead to vitamin A and D poisoning. Polar bear liver may contain nearly 2,000,000 units of vitamin A per 100 gm, which approaches the concentration in halibut-liver oil, and this would appear to account for its toxicity, as also in the case of Arctic fox and seal, whale and shark liver.

In general the liquid oils of marine origin (fatty acid composition; Review, 1965), and of vegetable origin tend to lower serum cholesterol levels. Animal and other hard fats tend to raise the levels (see also Dietary Factors and Blood Lipids).

Chapter 5

FOOD ADDITIVES

$\mathbf{F}$ood additives are substances without any nutritive value that are intentionally added to enhance the taste, structure, or storage life of food. They include a great variety of substances which include acidifiers, alkalizers, antibiotics, anti-caking, anti-oxidant, bleaching, coloring, curing, emulsifying, flavoring, humectant (moisture-retaining), leavening, maturing, preservative, stabilizing, sweetening, thickening and vitamin compounds.

A definition of a food additive in regulations in the Food and Drugs Act in Canada is as follows:

Food additive means any substance, including any source of radiation, the use of which results, or may reasonably be expected to result in it or its by-products becoming part of or affecting the characteristics of a food, but does not include (i) any nutritive material that is used, recognized, or commonly sold as an article or ingredient of food, (ii) vitamins, mineral constituents and amino acids, (iii) spices, seasonings, flavouring preparations, essential oils, oleoresins and natural extractives, (iv) pesticides, (v) food packaging materials and components thereof, and (vi) drugs recommended for administration to animals that may be consumed as food.

Food additives may be added only to specified foods within permitted limits. A consideration of this problem is reviewed by Chapman and Morrison (1966). Chemical additives are considered in publications of the National Academy of Sciences (1965; 1966), in the *Extra Pharmacopoeia* (1967), and by workers mentioned in the following pages.

In a number of countries there has been careful and objective examination of the desirability and safety of these agents, and governments have obtained the opinion of appropriate expert organizations. There are regulations enacted by the authorities to protect consumers against harm and fraud associated with the sale and consumption of foods. There may be simple supervision or control over food sanitation and adulteration, or in the more developed countries legislation of wide scope and complexity as industries have developed, as consumers have become better informed, and as scientific advances have provided sound basis for regulation. Production, manufacture, labelling, packaging, advertising and the sale of foods are all controlled. There are many difficulties encountered by organizations dealing with the problem of safety of food additives (Day, 1960); these organizations include the food industry (Review, 1961). Major problems relating to the use of food additives and pesticides in the United States and Canada are reviewed in a Symposium on Additives and Residues (1961), and by Hueper (1961), Oser (1966) and Chapman and Morrison (1966); and problems relating to the provision of personnel to deal with toxicological problems as encountered in New Zealand are discussed by Barnes (1966).

There is some measure of international agreement on food and food products. The Joint FAO/WHO Expert Committee on Food Additives meets regularly and publishes reports (WHO Technical Reports on Food Additives) on many problems relating to intentional and unintentional food additives. The First Report was published in 1957 and the Ninth Report in 1966.

In England the Ministry of Agriculture, Fisheries and Food (1965) has indicated the tests which a new food would need to undergo before its use was permitted for sale. These tests are as follows: (a) composition, purity and commercial usage; (b) acute toxicity in certain laboratory animal species; (c) short-term studies in certain laboratory animals; (d) long-term studies including carcinogenicity, extending over the whole of the animal's life; (e) the metabolism including, where appropriate, its effects on enzymes; (f) the effect on man.

TYPES OF FOOD ADDITIVES

Food additives may be classified as follows:

    a. Flavoring agents, i.e., sweetening agents, acidifying agents, condiments.

    b. Coloring agents and decoloring agents, e.g., dyes, whitening agents, bleaching agents.

    c. Consistency - improving agents, e.g., emulsifying agents, frothing agents, softening agents, stabilizing agents, thickening agents.

    d. Preservatives, e.g., antioxidants, antibiotics, humectants.

Food additives may be classified also according to the functions for which they are commonly used:

    a. To improve the nutritive value, nutritional supplements may be added, e.g., vitamins in breakfast cereals, thiamine in bread, iodide in salt, fluoride in water.

    b. To enhance the flavor, e.g., salt, volatile oils, spices, sodium glutamate, amyl acetate.

    c. To maintain the appearance, palatability, and wholesomeness, by the addition of antibiotics, and antioxidants, e.g., ascorbic acid, butylated hydroxyanisole, and derivatives of propionic and citric acid.

    d. To impart and maintain a desired consistency, by the use of emulsifiers, stabilizers, thickeners, e.g., acacia, glycerides, lecithin, methylcellulose.

    e. To control the acidity or alkalinity in many processed foods, and as leavening agents in baking, e.g., citric, lactic and tartaric acids, potassium acid tartrate, sodium bicarbonate (in self-raising flour) .

    f. To give a desired color, by using certain natural substances, e.g., carotene, chlorophyll, cochineal, or synthetic dyes.

    g. To act as maturing agents and bleaching agents of the yellow pigments of wheat (bread improvers) and of certain cheeses, e.g., chlorine, chlorine dioxide, nitrosyl chloride, potassium bromate and iodate.

h. To perform other special functions, such as to retain moisture (humectants), e.g., glycerin; to keep salts and powders free-flowing (anti-caking), e.g., magnesium carbonate; as curing agents for meat, e.g., nitrates, nitrites, nicotinic acid; as sweetening agents, e.g., calcium and sodium cyclamates, saccharin.

The following are a few examples of some foods and the permitted additives that are used:

a. Bread, cake, cheese and pie may contain sodium proprionate and sorbic acid (2,4-hexadienoic acid), used to protect the material against fungi.

b. Cherries, strawberries may contain chlorinated trisodium phosphate.

c. Melons may contain sodium dimethyl dithiocarbamate (2 per cent in wax applied to the surface).

d. Poultry (freshly killed, to be cooked) may contain oxytetracycline, and chlorinated trisodium phosphate.

e. Animals feeds may contain antibiotics, sodium propionate and other additives.

Antibiotics, antioxidants, dyes, flavoring agents, iodine, methylcellulose, mineral hydrocarbons, preservatives, salt, sweetening agents and animal feeds are considered in more detail in the following sections.

ANTIBIOTICS

Certain countries, for example the United States, Chile and Japan, have allowed the use of oxytetracycline and chlortetracycline for the storage and transport of deep-sea fish and poultry, with permissible residual values of five to seven parts per million. These antibiotics act as preservatives for freshly caught non-processed fish, scallops and unpeeled shrimp, and for uncooked poultry. A few countries have permitted beef to be treated with antibiotics injected into the animal immediately prior to slaughter and by surface application to the carcasses. Whales have been preserved by injection of antibiotic intraperitoneally after killing, or by including antibiotic in the head of the harpoon. Nisin is used in processed cheese and in certain canned foods. Nystatin has been applied to the skin of bananas to control molds; it does not penetrate the fruit.

There is the fear in certain quarters that this use of antibiotics may lead to the emergence of resistant pathogenic bacteria transmissible to man, and possibly to direct harmful effects and hypersensitivity reactions from the consumption of food containing such antibiotics. Details about the use of antimicrobials for the preservation of food are given by Vaughn and Stewart (1960), and by the Joint FAO/WHO Expert Committee which has published a number of reports on this subject, most recently the Ninth Report (1966). The use of antibiotics in food to increase the growth rate especially in pigs and chickens is considered in a later section dealing with animal feeds.

ANTIOXIDANTS

Food substances that are subject to oxidation include unsaturated oils and fats and vitamins. The oxidation reactions can be inhibited by antioxidants which are of two kinds: (a) true antioxidants such as ascorbic acid, 3-buty-5-hydroxyanisole (BHA), and the tocopherols; (b) antioxidant synergists, which are chelating agents such as citric acid and thiodipropionic acid derivatives (dilauryl thiodipropionate and distearyl thiodipropionate). Other antitoxidants are citric acid esters, for example propyl citrate, benzoate and mono- and di-glycerides of fat-forming fatty acids which are used in margarine, benzoin in lard, and guaiac in oils and fats.

A review of the uses of antioxidants in food is given by Lea (1952), and in the *Extra Pharmacopoeia* (1967). They include the prevention of rancidity in fats, the stabilization of edible oils and fats, and the prevention of darkening of certain fresh fruits when cut and exposed to the air prior to processing.

In England and Scotland the use of these preservatives is controlled by The Antioxidant in Food Regulations, 1958. The foods to which they may be added are the following: (a) anhydrous edible oils and fats and vitamin oils and concentrates; (b) butter for manufacturing purposes, and (c) essential oils and their flavoring constituents.

A table indicating acceptable daily intakes for man of some antioxidants (and antimicrobials) is given in the Ninth Report of the Joint FAO/WHO Expert Committee on Food Additives (1966).

DYES, COLORING AGENTS

Coloring materials from natural sources have been used in foods since ancient times. They have now been largely superseded by synthetic dyes which are available in a wider range of more stable colors. The agents used are subject to legislative control in many countries, but this varies considerably; some dyes may be permitted in one country but are officially forbidden in another country. No dye is universally permitted. It is regrettable that the lists of approved dyes should vary so much in individual countries. A useful review of the dyes used in foods and drugs is available in the *Extra Pharmacopoeia* (1967).

In the United States the use of coloring matters is controlled by regulations issued under the Federal Food, Drug, and Cosmetic Act, and a list of coal-tar colors approved for use is issued under the title of F.D. & C. Colors. There are lists issued also for colors approved for use in drugs and cosmetics but not in food.

In England and Scotland the recommendations of The Food Standards Committee are presented in the Colouring Matter in Food Regulations, 1957, and in a Report on the Review of these regulations published in 1964 and in 1966.

In Australia colors permitted were published as Statutory Rules 1963 No. 115, under the Health Act 1958. In the European Economic Community a directive governing the use of coloring matters in food was issued in 1962 by the Council of the Community; previously each country had its own permitted list. In South Africa there are regulations under the Food, Drugs, and Disinfectants Act, No. 13 of 1929.

The FAO/WHO Expert Committee on Food Additives has published details about dyes for coloring foods. Many dyes have been classified according to toxicological evaluation. Only three dyes were found to be acceptable for use in food, *viz.* amaranth, sunset yellow FCF, and tartrazine, and twelve were considered harmful and not to be used: auramine, butter yellow, chrysoidine, Guinea green B, magenta, oil orange SS, oil orange XO, oil yellow AB, oil yellow OB, ponceau 3R, ponceau SX, Sudan 1 (Eighth Report of Expert Committee, 1965). Specifications of many dyes used for coloring foods have been published by the FAO/WHO for the guidance of manufacturers and users of these substances, and as a basis for legislation in countries dealing locally with these problems (*Specifications for Identity and Purity of Food Additives*, Vol. II: *Food Colours*, 1963).

In England new regulations published in the Colouring Matter in Food Regulations, 1966, now include the recommendations previously made by The Food Standards Committee in its Report in 1964 that the following six dyes be deleted from the British list, *viz.*, Ponceau SX, Ponceau 3R, Naphthol Yellow S, Yellow RFS, Yellow RY, Blue VRS, and that Black 7984 be added to the list.

Synthetic dyes that are permitted for use in foods and beverages are provisionally regarded as harmless, but constant investigation and surveillance are required. A number of compounds previously allowed have been withdrawn and their use prohibited by law because of toxicity, including carcinogenicity and teratogenicity, that was subsequently recognized; for example, carcinogenic amines and the dyes produced from them have been used for many years as certified colors in food, drugs and cosmetics. Some have been "decertified" as in the case of yellow AB and yellow OB, which were previously used for years for coloring butter, margarine and cheese, but others have been retained. Food dyes with recognized or suspected carcinogenic potentiality are listed and considered by Hueper (1961; 1962). Certain artificial food colors are known to have caused urticaria in children who had eaten colored candies (sweets), and on rare occasions severe asthma has occurred from sensitivity to tartrazine and certain other dyes commonly used to color many foods as well as drug tablets and capsules.

An internationally agreed list of dyes has become a great need with the increase in universal trade in food. This matter has received detailed consideration at international level by the joint commission FAO/WHO.

FLAVORING AGENTS

Many foods are by nature tasteless or unpleasant without some added substance to make them more appetizing. Since earliest times there has been an extensive trade and use of spices such as allspice or pimento, asafoetida, cassia, cayenne, cinnamon, cloves, coriander, cumin, garlic, ginger, mustard, nutmeg and pepper. Information about condiments and spices is available in many books, for example Nicholls, Sinclair and Jelliffe (1961) Antia (1966), Hall (1966), *Extra Pharmacopoeia* (1967). These agents have a carminative effect and decrease the flatulence which tends to arise from pulses and coarse vegetables. Herbs also such as bay leaves, rosemary, sage, savory, origanum and thyme have been much used in the culinary art. The use in general of the spices, salt, sweetening agents, essential oils, vinegar and a number of other substances is well known.

Essential oils and carminatives used as spices and preservatives for food, and for other purposes, are complex mixtures and consist largely of hydrocarbons. Taken internally they produce a mild irritant action in the mouth and digestive tract, increased salivation and a feeling of warmth. They may cause some increase in bronchial secretion as they are excreted by the lungs; they exert some stimulant action on respiration and the heart. Taken after a meal they exert a carminative action, i.e., they permit the eructation of gas from the stomach; this is due partly to the production of local congestion and swelling of the mucosal valve at the lower end of the esophagus which thus causes interference with the neat closure of the valve, and partly due to relaxation of the sphincter. They tend also to counteract flatulent colic, and the colic produced by purgative substances. Large doses irritate the kidneys, bladder and urethra. The excessive intake of Worcestershire sauce has been reported as causing bilateral renal calculi and aminoaciduria possibly due to its content of potentially nephrotoxic ingredients such as acetic acid, garlic, black pepper, ginger, allspice, mace and cinnamon, or to some other constituent of the sauce (Murphy, 1967).

Synthetic imitation flavors are much used in the preparation of foods and sweets, for example acetylacetate (orange flavor) and propylacetate (pear flavor) are used to flavor boiled sweets. Many chemicals are added to proprietary brands of food to make them more appetizing and attractive, for example glutamic acid from wheat gluten gives a strong meaty flavor to soups and stews. This amino acid is normally utilized by the body cells.

Natural products should be used in preference to synthetic chemicals. However, the widespread addition of many different kinds of chemicals has come to stay, and it is the function of special institutions to investigate all such agents to ensure that they are not injurious. Different measures are adopted in different countries. Thus in England, recommendations have been made by The Food Standards Committee of the Ministry of Agriculture, Fisheries and Food (Report on Flavouring Agents, 1965) that the following substances should be prohibited for use in food: coumarin, tonka bean, safrole, dihydrosafrole, isosafrole, sassafras oil, agaric acid, nitrobenzene, dulcamara, pennroyal oil, oil of tansy, rue oil, birch tar oil, cade oil, volatile bitter almond oil, male fern (*Extra Pharmacopoeia*, 1967).

In the United States the Food and Drug Administration operating under the Federal laws regulating food additives aims to protect consumers from the presence of hazardous chemicals (Arena, 1963). Thus for example, studies by the F.D.A. (U.S.A.) have shown that safrole, a constituent of sassafras and the essential oils of cinnamon, nutmeg and mace, and once widely used as a flavoring agent, is carcinogenic in rats; it produces hepatic adenomas in rats with deficient diets, testicular atrophy and depression of the bone marrow (Gleason *et al.*, 1963). Safrole was once used to flavor root beer, sarsaparilla and other beverages; this has been discontinued. However the use of cinnamon, nutmeg and other natural substances containing low levels of safrole is permitted (Kraybill, 1963). The advisability of investigating for carcinogenic properties all of the approximately three hundred flavoring agents currently in use in the preparation and processing of foods was indicated by Hueper (1962).

IODINE COMPOUNDS

Iodides and iodates in table salt and certain liquids and foods have been extensively used in the prophylaxis of endemic goiter (see Water). They do not appear to have caused any harm when used in the correctly recommended amounts. Many authors have reported untoward effects from the administration of large doses (Department of Nutrition, 1955). An iodine-containing coloring agent that has been permitted for use in food is erythrosine (sodium tetraiodofluorescein), for example to impart a red color to maraschino cherries.

METHYLCELLULOSE

This white fibrous compound is odorless and tasteless. It is extensively used in food preparations. It dissolves in water to form a jelly. It is not absorbed from the intestine, and although it does not appear to interfere with the absorption of vitamins and other nutrients, this is a subject still requiring long-term investigation.

Taken by mouth in doses of 5 gm twice daily it increases the water and bulk of the stools by about ten times the weight of the drug. The estimated acceptable daily intake for man is up to 30 mg per kg body weight (Seventh Report of FAO/WHO on Food Additives 1964).

MINERAL HYDROCARBONS

Liquid paraffin (liquid petrolatum) (mineral oil) as a substitute for olive oil is now prohibited as it prevents the absorption of fat-soluble vitamins and has other disadvantages. A small amount of mineral oil is absorbed and it has been suggested that this may be a cause of hitherto poorly explained pathology in the reticulo-endothelial system, i.e., in the lymph nodes, spleen and other tissues (Review, 1967). According to Hueper (1962) the frequent ingestion of insufficiently refined mineral oils of various derivation presents a carcinogenic hazard to the intestine.

In England and Scotland the use of any mineral hydrocarbon in the composition or preparation of food is prohibited in terms of The Mineral Hydrocarbons in Food Regulations 1966; exemptions are dried fruit (0.5 per cent), citrus fruit (0.1 per cent), sugar confectionery (0.2 per cent), any chewing compound (60 per cent of solid mineral hydrocarbon), the rind of any whole pressed cheese, and eggs through dipping or spraying for preserving. The mineral hydrocarbons used must comply with the specification in the Regulations.

PRESERVATIVES

Antimicrobial agents that may be added to particular foods in specific maximum proportions include benzoic acid or its sodium or potassium salt, copper carbonate, certain hydroxybenzoates, nitrates, nitrites, sorbic acid or certain of its salts, sulphurous acid or certain of its salts, and tetracyclines.

The substances that may be added as preservatives in foods are severely restricted by law. The estimated acceptable daily intake for man of these and other preservatives is given in the Sixth Report of FAO/WHO on Food Additives 1962.

In England benzoic acid and its sodium salt, sulphur dioxide and certain sulphites are permitted by law (The Preservatives in Food Regulations 1962), but a number of other substances which are not considered to be preservatives in law are used freely. These include salt, sugars, lactic acid, acetic acid, glycerol, alcohol, herbs, spices and essential oils. Sodium nitrate is permitted in limited amounts, but only with bacon, ham and cooked meats. In Canada a wider choice is permitted and includes propionic and sorbic acids and sodium diacetate, and in the United States penicillin and chlortetracycline have also been included.

Benzoic acid and sodium benzoate have largely been replaced by other derivatives of this acid, for example methyl hydroxybenzoate and propyl hydroxybenzoate, which are extensively used in Europe. Sulphur dioxide has been used in the preservation of dried fruit, fruit juice and fruit pulp. Sodium nitrite is permitted in meat, for example in South Africa the allowed maximum is 200 ppm. Potassium nitrate and the nitrite are permitted in New

South Wales in various kinds of meat and sausages. Nitrites added as a preservative to herring meal lead to the formation of nitrosamines (Sakshaug *et al.,* 1965); these are being much studied as carcinogens (*q.v.*)

Boric acid and borax are unsafe for use in food.

Antibiotics such as the tetracyclines are permissible in certain countries as preservatives for uncooked poultry and freshly caught fish, as indicated in the separate note on antibiotics (see above). Their use presents a number of public health problems, especially in causing the development of allergy, hypersensitivity and the evolution of resistant strains of organisms. Antioxidants used to prevent changes in certain foods such as oils, fats, vitamins and essential oils are considered in the separate note on antioxidants (see above).

Ionizing radiation for the preservation and processing of food is technically feasible, and food so treated under specified conditions is suitable for consumption by animals and man. No evidence of radiation-induced toxicity or carcinogenicity has been found. It seems that irradiation of foods may become of widespread commercial interest in the future. There have been numerous publications dealing with investigations on the effect of irradiation of many kinds of food. The subject has been considered by a committee of experts (*WHO tech. Rep. Ser. No.* 316, 1966). An annotated bibliography of abstracts of 311 publications has been published by Reber *et al.* (1966) and a review of the toxicological safety of irradiated foods by Kraybill and Whitehair (1967). The possible applications of this method of food preservation have been also considered by Goldblith (1967).

SALT

Normal salt balance depends on an equality of the amount of sodium excreted and the amount ingested. Details about physiological requirements and about disturbances that occur from excessive retention or loss in certain diseased states may be found in textbooks dealing with pharmacology and therapy.

Excessive intake of salt can cause poisoning. It has occurred in infants from the substitution of salt (sodium chloride) for sugar, it produces vomiting, respiratory distress and convulsions, and death can occur (Finberg *et al.*, 1963; Calvin *et al.*, 1964). The experimental work and other evidence relating to the possible adverse effects of prolonged intake of salt is reviewed by Meneely (1966).

A low salt intake or the elimination of salt by oral diuretics is an important consideration, together with other measures, in the management of congestive heart failure, and it can produce a decrease in blood pressure in patients with hypertension. The corollary is not established, namely that a high intake of salt is a cause of hypertension, although this may explain the high incidence of hypertension in Japan (Dahl, 1960). Exessive deficiency of sodium chloride can produce symptoms (salt depletion syndrome).

Salt Substitutes

These may contain such substances as potassium chloride, ammonium chloride, calcium phosphate, glutamic acid, ammonium glutamate, mono-potassium glutamate, glycine, magnesium citrate, potassium or calcium formate.

Lithium chloride was widely used at one time as a substitute for common salt in low-sodium diets. Untoward reactions occurred when the serum-lithium concentration was above 1 mEq per liter in association with a depletion of serum sodium (Talbott, 1950). Many of the symptoms ascribed to lithium poisoning could be due to sodium chloride deficiency. The leaf of *Oxalis* spp. (sorrel) has sometimes been used by the Zulu in Southern Africa as a salt substitute in cooking.

SWEETENING AGENTS

For the majority of people, sucrose has been the sweetening agent of choice; it has advantages and disadvantages (see below). Diabetic subjects and those on reducing diets may only use sweetening agents that do not raise their blood sugar or increase their calorie intake. Various synthetic sweetening agents sweeter than or comparable in sweetness with sugar are available, for example cyclamates, saccharin and sorbitol (Brookes, 1965).

$$CH_2OH$$
$$HCOH$$
$$HOCH$$
$$HCOH$$
$$HCOH$$
$$CH_2OH$$

NHSO$_3$Na

Cyclamate
sodium

Saccharin
sodium

D—Sorbitol

Cyclamates

Sodium cyclamate and calcium cyclamate (Sucaryl®) which are salts of cyclamic acid (cyclohexylsulphamic acid) are used as sweetening agents, and subject to certain conditions are permitted to be used as artificial sweeteners. The Food Additives and Contaminants Committee in the United Kingdom accepts that there is no risk to health in allowing the use of cyclamates in food without limitation except for soft drinks and ice cream.

When used in a high concentration (0.5 per cent) in food cyclamates tend to be bitter in taste. No adverse effects are reported from the continued use of small amounts, but there is no certainty that large amounts can be safely taken over long periods. Mushy and frequent stools occur when large amounts, 5 gm or more, are ingested daily for a prolonged period; in some persons 0.1 gm daily may produce soft stools. This action is probably due to osmotic effects of unabsorbed cyclamate causing bulky stools.

Saccharin

This synthetic agent is extensively used as a substitute for sucrose. Subject to certain conditions it is a permitted artificial sweetener for soft drinks. It has no food value. It is excreted almost quantitatively without undergoing metabolic transformation. It produces a decrease in the blood sugar level of normal persons (Kun and Horvath, 1947).

Pharmacological, toxicological and clinical investigations have shown that the continuous use of small amounts of saccharin is virtually harmless. Large doses daily may produce hyperacidity;

5 to 25 gm daily or a single dose of 100 gm may cause anorexia, nausea, vomiting and diarrhea, abdominal pain, spasm of muscles, convulsions and stupor. In hypersensitive persons saccharin may even in small doses produce vomiting, diarrhea and skin eruptions.

Sorbitol

This six-carbon polyhydric alcohol $CH_2.OH$ $(CH.OH)_4.$-$CH_2.OH$ is an isomer of mannitol (manna sugar). It occurs in small quantities in certain fruits such as apples, cherries, mountain-ash berries, pears and plums, and it is also made synthetically. It is about half as sweet as sugar. It is virtually nontoxic even when given intravenously in doses of 50 to 100 gm. Excessive doses by mouth are laxative (Review, 1956), but in a dose of 25 gm daily it does not have this effect in most people. It has been shown to increase the absorption of paracetamol and iron preparations and to facilitate the transfer of nutrients across the placenta.

Since it does not produce a rise in blood sugar when given by mouth it may be taken by diabetics in doses up to 30 gm daily in place of sugar. It has been used in so-called sugarless dietetic candy, which may produce abdominal distension, gas and diarrhea. In patients with uncontrolled diabetes it may aggravate the hyperglycemia.

Glycerin

This trihydric alcohol has a sweet taste. When taken orally it is readily absorbed and provides calories. It has been used in place of syrups as a sweetening agent.

Glycerin has low toxicity. Human beings have been given 100 gm a day for fifty days without harm (Drill, 1965). Large doses are given by mouth in patients with acute closed-angle glaucoma, and with magnesium sulphate and saline to remove intestinal worms. However, systemic toxic effects have been noted when very large doses were given; they include restlessness, vomiting, purgation, fever, convulsions, hemoglobinuria, circulatory failure, coma and death after several hours.

Sugar (Sucrose)

This sweetening agent, so abundantly used, may be obtained from the juice of the sugar cane or white-rooted varieties of the sugar beet. It contains no vitamins or minerals. It provides calories, but has been condemned as a food substance.

Studies of the diet in various population groups have suggested that as more refined carbohydrates are added to the diet and more complex carbohydrates such as starches are eliminated there tends to be an increased incidence of coronary heart disease. Changes in the type of carbohydrate can produce changes in the lipids present in the tissues (Review, 1965). Sugar is a potent lipemic agent, as compared with starches, and a high dietary sugar intake may well be an important factor in the production of hyperglyceridemia and in the possible interrelation between diet, hyperglyceridemic hyperlipidemia and coronary artery disease (Macdonald, 1964; Kuo and Bassett, 1965; Review, 1965, 1966). Rifkind *et al.* (1966) have recently indicated further that dietary sucrose may regulate serum-triglyceride levels and that it may have a causative role in ischemic heart disease. Much work has been done experimentally and clinically to prove that a high consumption of sugar is an important factor in the causation of ischemic heart disease and that a person taking a large amount of sugar has a greatly increased chance of developing myocardial infarction (Yudkin and Roddy, 1966; Yudkin, 1967). It must also be added that coffee elevates serum lipids in susceptible persons (Little *et al.*, 1966), and that the relationship between alcohol, heart disease and liver disease has also to be considered.

According to the conception of Cleave and Campbell (1966), the consumption of artificially refined carbohydrates, for example white or brown sugar and white flour, may be responsible for a group of very different clinical conditions. They consider these may all be manifestations of one central disease, "saccharine disease," which includes dental caries and paradontal disease (pyorrhea); gastric and duodenal ulcer and other forms of indigestion; obesity, diabetes mellitus and coronary disease; colonic stasis (constipation) with its complications of varicose veins and hemorrhoids; probably primary *Bacillus coli* infections such as cholecystitis, and certain skin disorders. These workers consider that the many different manifestations are dependent on personal build in the parts of the body concerned. Sugar has been mainly incriminated as a cause of the disease since it is the most refined of the carbohydrates, but refined flour is also emphasized as an important causal factor of "saccharine disease." For references to the role of sugar in the etiology of the various disorders mentioned the monograph of Cleave and Campbell (1966) should be consulted. Claims have been made that calcium sucrose phosphate, which is tasteless and harmless, is effective in preventing dental caries.

ANIMAL FEEDS

It has become widespread practice in a number of countries to add nutritional substances and also drugs as supplements to animal feeds in order to stimulate and improve growth and to control disease. Six principal groups of additives are officially recognized in this regard: antibiotics, synthetic hormones, minerals, anti-infection agents and vitamins (British Veterinary Codex 1965, Appendix 16). A long list of additives such as antibiotics, arsenicals, estrogens, coccidiostats and a variety of other compounds that were officially recognized is given by Bird (1961).

The antibiotics that are now permitted in food include small quantities of penicillin or certain tetracyclines, and also other antibiotics in some countries (WHO *techn. Rep. Ser., No.* 260, 1963 [see below]; Sarkisov, 1966). It is not only poultry (except ducks and geese) and pigs that benefit from antibiotic feeding but also calves, beef, cattle, lambs, rabbits and fur-bearing animals such as mink. The antibiotics promote growth probably by suppressing pathogenic organisms in the gastrointestinal tract, they improve the conversion of food, and reduce mortality rate in the growing animals. There is the possibility with the use of these antimicrobinal agents of the development of permanent antibiotic-resistant bacteria. Also, in adult ruminants they may impair normal processes of bacterial fermentation and may cause digestive disturbances including a loss of appetite. No detectable amounts of the recommended antibiotics have been found in the liver and muscle of poultry and pigs; traces that may be present are readily destroyed by cooking. Thus the antibiotics in feeds would not appear to be harmful to the animals themselves. The potential hazard arises from the effect of the antibiotics on bacteria. The possibility that the use of antibiotics in feeds may prejudice their therapeutic use in man is a cause for concern (Report of the Joint Committee on Antibiotics in Animal Feeding, Agricultural Research Council and M.R.C., H.M. Stationery Office, 1962). The problem has recently been discussed at a meeting arranged by the National Research Council—National Academy of Sciences at the behest of the United States Food and Drug Administration.

Although the antibiotics used for the treatment of animal diseases do not normally lead to accumulation of the drugs in the tissues the WHO Expert Committee has nevertheless recommended that an interval should be allowed between the last administration of drug and the time of slaughter. The Committee also recommends that eggs from poultry receiving therapeutic amounts of antibiotics should not be sold for human consumption (Report of Expert Committee on the Public Health Aspects of Food and Feedstuffs, WHO *tech. Rep. Ser. No.* 260, 1963).

Synthetic estrogens administered in the feed or by implantation are usually stilbestrol or hexestrol. Before marketing poultry carcasses the portion of the neck containing an implant must first be removed. The estrogens are used to stimulate growth and weight of cattle, sheep, poultry and pigs, and to produce increased deposition of fat in poultry. Prolonged administration in male animals tends to produce female behavior. Because of the suspected carcinogenic effect, the use of stilbestrol as implants in cockerels was prohibited in South Africa in 1954 (Government Notice 2517, Section 13b), and a similar ruling was made in 1958 by the Food and Drug Administration in the United States.

Copper added to the food ration of pigs in Great Britain has been found to improve weight gains and food efficiency. In the United States and Australia toxic effects have resulted from the addition of copper to the animal feeds. Investigations are in progress to elucidate an explanation for the differences observed in the different countries (Review, 1966). Methylthiouracil has been used as an aid in fattening animals such as pigs and steers but the reported results are conflicting.

Irradiation of feeds intended for consumption by animals has been investigated in recent years (Kraybill and Whitehair, 1967). Such irradiated food should be subject to control by procedures analogous to those used for the control of irradiated food for human consumption. Food derived from animals reared and fed on suitably irradiated diets has not revealed detectable changes in their tissues nor in the tissues of their offspring (Report on The Technical Basis for Legislation on Irradiated Food, *WHO techn. Rep. Ser., No.* 316, 1966).

Chapter 6

FOOD CONTAMINANTS

Food contaminants are substances of natural or man-made origin that have inadvertently become included in food, and they may then produce unwanted effects. Many preparations used inside or outside the home may in this way be dangerous if taken internally, and they are not always labelled as being poisonous. Rat poison containing barium carbonate or arsenic, cockroach poison containing sodium fluoride, and vermin poison containing strychnine or barium salts have on many occasions been accidentally incorporated in meal or flour. Insecticides used in the home may also come to be present in food. Metallic compounds may reach food. This can occur in different ways: (a) by accidental mixing, e.g., when food is prepared in containers of unknown origin; (b) by solution from utensils in which they are processed; (c) from addition to the food, e.g., pesticides such as lead arsenate; (d) from natural sources, e.g., some marine products contain metal that may subsequently be released when they are prepared as food. Contamination of foods with poisonous metallic salts is considered in some detail and with references to many cases of poisoning by Dewberry (1959).

Some examples of unintentional contamination of food are given by Wogan (1966). For example, the disease of cattle known as "bovine hyperkeratosis" has been caused by chlorinated naphthalenes from lubricating oil; neurological disturbances and death have occurred in the inhabitants of Minamata Bay (Japan) who ate fish contaminated with mercury present in the effluent of a chemical factory; "chick hydropericardium" disease is probably due to chlorinated compounds in fats and oils.

127

According to some investigators, it is possible for illness including the development of carcinoma to occur in man from the ingestion over a long period of meat and fish that have been heavily smoked or subjected to deep-fat frying. More information is required as to the significance of this type of contamination produced by usual domestic cooking methods.

A number of important contaminants of food have been considered in other sections of this book. They include hepatotoxins, such as the *Senecio* alkaloids that have occasionally become incorporated in bread and the mycotoxins produced by certain fungi growing in groundnut meal; also the paralytic shellfish toxin that is occasionally present in mussels that have stored poisonous plankton in their digestive glands; and various household poisons including pesticides and metals derived from containers in which acid foods and fruit juices have been prepared.

Contaminants may be found in food (a) because they have intentionally been used on plants and have then persisted in the plants or in the soil in which they have grown; (b) because they have inadvertently been retained in food, after processing, preserving and packing; or (c) because of accidental pollution of certain areas of soil and water and therefore of animals and plants, for example by pesticides and radionuclides.

Considered in somewhat more detail it is evident that contaminants or harmful impurities may enter food directly or indirectly as follows:

a. From the application of insecticides and fungicides to growing vegetables and fruit.

b. From contamination of soil by herbicides and weed killers applied primarily to vegetables, grain and orchards; from substances added to the soil itself; or from accidental presence in the soil of radioactive material.

c. From the use of substances in animal feeds, to stimulate growth of the animals, for example antibiotics and hormones.

d. From the processing of food with additives that may contain noxious substances.

e. From drugs used in the treatment of disease in animals, for example penicillin in cow's milk.

f. From the use of insecticides, fungicides and rodenticides in cow stalls, barns and other places where food is stored and protected.

g. From substances in the packaging material.

The foreign substances that may be present in foodstuffs have been considered by Kühnau (1960), Hueper (1961), Roe and Lancaster (1964), Miller and Miller (1965), and at a number of Symposia held in recent years (Symposia 1965, 1966). The extent to which the human body is exposed to such dangerous influences as have been mentioned above has been difficult to gauge.

MYCOTOXINS AND MYCOTOXICOSIS

These have become very significant because there are foodstuffs that can provide a favorable medium for the growth of molds. Once the mycotoxins have been produced they remain in the food even though the mold be subsequently destroyed by sterilization. A good example of this problem is provided by the fungal metabolites known as aflatoxins which are produced by molds such as *Aspergillus flavus* that may infect peanuts. These toxins are extremely potent hepatotoxic and hepatocarcinogenic agents, more powerful than benzpyrene and dimethylnitrosamine (Feuell, 1966). Aflatoxins and other mycotoxins have been much implicated in fatal diseases of farm stock fed infected peanut meal. There are relatively few examples of direct human involvement by mycotoxins, and these include poisoning by mushrooms, ergotism, yellow rice toxicity and alimentary toxic aleukia.

It is fortunate that the aflatoxins have intensely fluorescent properties that make their detection and estimation feasible even when there are extremely low levels; ochratoxin also is highly fluorescent. It is most important that molds be detected in foods and feeding-stuffs by suitable practical sampling and examination techniques, confirmed in selected instances by chemical or biological assay. The types of mycotoxicity that occur in feeds and foods are mentioned by Forgacs (1966) and Wilson (1966).

ANTIBIOTICS

These substances may be present in food, and there are five ways in which they may come to be there (Garrod, 1965) : (a) naturally present antibiotics, as in the preparation of cheese; (b) preservation of flesh foods with tetracyclines, as in the case of fish in trawlers' tanks, butchers' meat (permitted in Argentina) and eviscerated poultry (permitted in Canada and the United States) ; (c) supplement in animal feed; (d) prevention or treatment of intestinal infections in animals; (e) treatment of bovine mastitis. It is the latter use that presents the most serious problem since the antibiotics that are used are excreted in the milk, with possible risks to human health as is well known in the case of penicillin.

PESTICIDES

These are of great variety and include insecticides, fungicides, weed killers containing arsenic or copper or other substances, rodenticides for example 2-naphthylthiourea, sodium fluoroacetate and, very important, a large number of organic compounds, for example chlorinated hydrocarbons and organic phosphate esters. They may gain entry into food. Their widespread use as sprays on crops and for other purposes has caused them in general to become a potential menace to health, and in fact they have been responsible for many deaths in man and animals. A striking presentation of facts relating to toxic substances and ecological cycles has been published by Woodwell (1967).

The content of pesticide in food will vary to a great extent according to such factors as the nature of the pest control treatment originally used in seed preparation, spraying and sprinkling, weathering, climate and soil conditions. Untreated plants may also absorb pesticides from the soil.

Certain chlorinated hydrocarbons such as gamma benzene hexachloride (lindane) and chlorophenothane (dicophane; DDT) may remain in the soil for years, and they may remain in raw food for a long time (Review, 1960). Also, the organo-chlorine insecticides are stored for prolonged periods in the body fat and possibly in the liver of man and animal, after they have been absorbed from contaminated food; this applies especially to DDT, aldrin and dieldrin. They have also been investigated in a wide range of marine organisms (Robinson *et al.,* 1967). There appears to have been no acute danger in man, since the absorption of DDT from various food sources has been much less than the minimum toxic dose, and while there is the possibility of cumulative effects, DDT is not yet regarded as a serious poison for mammals (Review, 1967). Nevertheless it seems undesirable to countenance the presence of insecticide in the body fat if this can be avoided. The ingestion of aldrin with vegetables is important. It has been demonstrated in animals to produce a remarkable increase in the weight of the liver, but it remains to be determined whether such effects occur in man, whether they are harmless, and what would be the reaction of such (hypertrophied) liver to shock, infections, operations and drugs.

Many of the pesticides that may be present in agricultural products, fruits and vegetables, hay and forage crops, are listed in the encyclopedic volume published by Gleason, Gosselin and Hodge (1963). The information is most valuable as a guide to the chemist and the physician, although in the nature of things it is not always correct. Different conditions in different countries— agricultural, climatic and geographic—will produce differences in the degree and kind of food contamination.

The toxicity of pesticides and their residues in food have been reviewed by Hodges (1965). Some references to reports on residues in the body and in the diet are presented, with abstracts from the literature, in the *Extra Pharmacopoeia* (1967).

Constant surveillance is required to ensure that foodstuffs containing pesticides remain harmless for human consumption. This matter has been considered in a report on principles governing consumer safety in relation to pesticide residues (**WHO** *techn. Rep. Ser. No.* 240, 1962).

RADIONUCLIDES

Radioactive materials from natural or man-made sources for example radioactive fallout, can directly or indirectly contaminate vegetables, fruit, cereals and other foods (Review, 1961, 1963; Bird, 1966; Russell, 1966; Comar, 1966; Woodwell, 1967).

Milk and meat obtained from cattle that have eaten contaminated herbage present a danger to man. In England the milk supply has been analyzed every two weeks for radioactive strontium, iodine and cesium, as well as for stable calcium and potassium.

Strontium-90 (half-life of 28 years) has contaminated vegetables either by falling directly on foliage or by reaching the soil and entering the plants via the roots. Because of its long half-life it is one of the more dangerous isotopes formed during the fission of uranium in nuclear explosions. After ingestion by animal or man the strontium in food is absorbed and is stored particularly and almost permanently in the bones (Review, 1961; Woodwell, 1967). The increase of this substance in food and in the human body has been accepted as being without acute danger to the population, but as with the pesticides there is the problem of prolonged exposure to the contaminant. Other radionuclides such as iodine-131, cesium-137 (half-life of 30 years) and zinc-65 that have been found in milk have been present in concentrations regarded also as being well below the maximum permissible amounts (see Milk).

The levels of strontium-90 and cesium-137 in Canadian milk examined during the period 1960-1964 were consistently higher than those in the United States and Britain. As a result of radioactive fallout in the Canadian North cesium-137 has become (preferentially) retained in lichens and other plant materials. These form the principal food components for reindeer and caribou at certain times of the year, with the result that their meat has become heavily contaminated with this radionuclide. Eskimo residents of the Canadian North who consume such meat have been found by studies involving whole body counting and urine examination to have high cesium-137 levels (Bird, 1966; Woodwell, 1967).

PROCESSING DEGRADATION PRODUCTS

In recent years investigators have concentrated on reactions caused in animals and man by toxic degradation products formed or introduced into food during its processing. Important contaminants of food are substances that may be present as the result of heating and smoking of food. The possibility of tumor induction is being appraised (Hueper, 1961; Kraybill, 1963; Review, 1965). Evidence has accumulated from various countries that frequent and prolonged consumption of meats, sausages and fish that have been submitted to smoking procedures may increase the liability to cancer of the alimentary canal, especially the stomach. Such smoked foods have been shown to contain 3,4-benzpyrene.

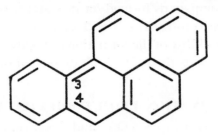

3,4 - benzpyrene

In Iceland it is customary in rural areas to preserve mutton and fish by a heavy smoking process; these foods then contain among other compounds a significant amount of 3,4-benzpyrene which is a carcinogen. Gastric cancer is common among the Icelandic population (Dungal, 1961).

Hueper (1962) has pointed out that the consumption of meat or fish broiled over an open fire carries a cancer hazard from contamination with carcinogenic soot and with carcinogens from the charred surface of the food. The products of the incomplete combustion of fat are known to contain a large number of polynuclear hydrocarbons including benzpyrenes and benzanthracenes. Such compounds have been detected on the surface of charcoal-broiled meat. Meat should not be broiled over the flames of burning fat. It may be cooked by the heat from the coals, not by the fire of a barbecue; any fires should be quickly extinguished by water. The F.D.A. has recommended that newspapers be not used as fuel for broiling (Questions and Answers, 1964).

A problem confronting food technologists concerned with the smoke curing process of animal and vegetable products is how to obtain desired amounts of compounds essential for the "smoky" flavor, and free from polycyclic hydrocarbons.

Chemicals used in processing of food may persist in the food or form harmful compounds. Thus trichloroethylene used as solvent in the preparation of decaffeinated coffee from green coffee beans may persist in the coffee even after the beans have been roasted (Brandenberger and Bader, 1967). The nature of the compound or compounds formed on interaction of trichloroethylene with coffee constituents is still unknown, but attention is drawn to the possibility of the formation of highly toxic S-dichlorovinyl derivatives as is the case in the extraction of soybeans with tricholorethylene.

CONTAMINATION FROM FOOD CONTAINERS

Baskets, boxes, cartons, crates and wood containers for fruit and vegetables may contain dieldrin, pyrethrins, or zinc petroleum sulphonate. Containers or wrappers of food containing adhesives, dyes, or plasticizers such as butylphthalate, may allow these to be leached and become mixed with the food. Plastics containing tri-orthocresyl phosphate may produce contamination of fatty foods stored in them and cause symptoms of poisoning. The lethal dose varies between 1 to 10 gm (Arena, 1963).

At a recent Symposium on Toxicity in Plastics (1967), participants considered the problems relating to potentially hazardous additives in plastics; such additives may migrate into food from materials in the manufacturing plant and from plastic food packaging and wrapping material.

Chapter 7

WATER, SOFT DRINKS, ALCOHOLIC BEVERAGES

Consideration is given in this section to water and a variety of beverages. Natural waters can be vehicles for substances that produce beneficial pharmacological effects. They may also be the cause of toxic effects. The increasing amounts of contaminants in natural waters that have come to be therein from human waste material and industrial waste and from the use of pesticides have been a cause of concern because of their adverse effects on plants and animal life as well as their possible adverse effects on man (Zapp and Clayton, 1963). It is recognized that in some parts of the world water may be harmful or potentially harmful because of excessive amounts of naturally-occurring substances such as fluorides and nitrates, or of contaminants such as algal toxins, pesticides, or radionuclides (Comar, 1966).

Cool (soft) drinks and fruit juices may damage tooth enamel because of their acid content, and occasionally they may be harmful because of other active substances present in them. Beverages such as tea and coffee, which contain caffeine and other principles, are also considered here from certain points of view, without details being given about the well-known pharmacological action of caffeine and related xanthine compounds.

Alcoholic beverages also are considered here, but not from the point of view of alcohol itself, the pharmacological actions of which are widely known. Reference is made to the reactions that may occur when alcoholic drinks are taken in combination with certain other substances, for example acetaldehyde intoxication may occur when alcohol is ingested with the inky cap fungus that contains disulfiram. A hypertensive action is produced by certain

135

wines such as Chianti when they are taken with antidepressive drugs such as the mono-amine oxidase inhibitors. Serious effects may well be caused by homemade Bantu beer and other intoxicating beverages prepared by certain population groups.

WATER

Water is the most abundant and a most important chemical substance in the body. The total volume of body water in man varies between 50 to 70 per cent of the body weight, closer to 50 per cent in the obese and closer to 70 per cent in lean individuals. The intake of water is derived from fluids in the diet, from solids in the diet that are greatly hydrated, and from the oxidation of hydrogen in food in the tissues. The quantity of liquid drunk depends on individual taste, but it is commonly less than the amount of water consumed as food. The minimal daily water requirement of a healthy adult is in the region of 1500 ml. Excessive water intake with properly functioning renal and adaptive mechanisms will not produce positive water balance and retention. This will result when there is circulatory or renal deficiency which interferes with the proper elimination of water. The signs of excessive hydration are related to the increased volume of water and also to its excess in relation to sodium content.

Acute water intoxication from compulsive or voluntary water drinking has been reported (Bewley, 1964; Dugan and Holliday, 1967). The symptoms include twitchings, convulsions and coma, probably due to cerebral edema.

The water taken at spas (natural springs) benefits many patients but this is usually attributed to the change of regimen and the inculcation of regular habits rather than to any special medicinal properties of the waters. Hard drinking water has been compared with soft water in relation to the incidence of atherosclerosis, and certain differences have been found (Review, 1967); these need to be confirmed and evaluated.

The presence of fluoride in excessive amounts in natural drinking water and food may cause brown to brownish-black discoloration or mottling of the tooth enamel and other changes in the body. In some areas, for example the North Western Cape region of South Africa, the fluoride excess in bore-hole water and well water may be a cause of endemic goiter (Department of Nutrition, 1955). On the other hand the intake of too little fluoride may be associated with a high incidence of dental caries, and fluoridation of pubic water supplies has been established to protect the teeth against caries, particularly in certain areas (Review, 1964). In certain countries it has been recommended that fluoride be included in solid and liquid food in an attempt to combat dental erosion.

Water and food are the major sources of iodine; but in most items of the diet this element is not abundant, the only rich sources being those derived from marine life. For those who do not eat fish, the element is scarce indeed (Goodman and Gilman, 1965). Most potable waters contain a negligible amount. In those areas where goiter is endemic, prophylactic medication with iodides or iodates has been most valuable, the most practicable method being the addition of iodide to table salt. In some countries this is enforced by law (the use of iodide in salt), in others including the United States the use is optional. In Japan none is needed because kelp is a national delicacy.

Nitrates and nitrites present in well water have occasionally produced poisoning; in artificially fed infants methemoglobinemia has occurred from the use of such water in the preparation of feeds (Locket, 1957; Steyn, 1960; Fassett, 1966). There were in the course of a period of three years 139 cases of nitrate poisoning (methemoglobinemia) in infants in Minnesota which resulted in fourteen deaths (Any Questions, 1965). The danger from toxic effects of nitrates in drinking-water seems to be restricted to infants of one year and under. The limit specified for nitrates in drinking-water in the United States is 45 mg per liter. Nitrates may be present not only in water but also in certain foods and plants; this is considered in other sections of this book.

Soft water can dissolve a coating of lead from the inside of lead pipes; peaty water with its content of various organic acids such as humic and ulmic acids, and a high bicarbonate and nitrate content, can have the same effect.

Certain plant materials present in water have caused poisoning in animals and human beings, for example the leaf and flower of *Nerium oleander L.* (Ceylon rose) have caused poisoning (Watt and Breyer-Bandwyk, 1962).

Toxic Phytoplankton (Blue-green Algae)

The sporadic growth of this fresh water plankton in lakes, dams and reservoirs has from time to time caused gastrointestinal symptoms and convulsions. Death has occurred in thousands of large-horned stock, sheep, horses, donkeys, dogs, also birds, water-fowl and ducks, for example in South Africa, Australia, the United States, the U.S.S.R. (Review, 1961). The accumulation of algal toxin in the bodies of fish has caused mass death of cats.

In South Africa the algal poisoning of animals and man has been studied by Steyn (1944). A review dealing with toxic phyto-plankton is available as a translation from a paper by a Soviet investigator (Vinberg, 1955); information is also given by Watt and Breyer-Bandwyk (1962).

The toxic principle is not fully investigated. It is relatively stable to heat and to extreme $_p$H values. It is an alkaloid. An important point to be noted is that the features of poisoning in animals, for example when experimentally-induced in cats, differ from those characteristic for human beings.

In man there is a condition known as Haff disease which is so named from its occurrence on the shores of the fresh water bay, Firsches Haff, on the Baltic Sea. It develops about eighteen hours after ingestion of toxic fresh water fish such as bream, tur-bot, eel, pike, perch and roach. It is characterized by muscle pains, paralysis, hemoglobinuria, and sometimes death from involvement of the diaphragm and other respiratory muscles. Sudden outbreaks of stomach and intestinal diseases of unexplained causation that have occurred in the region of river basins may have been due to water containing algae. The term *acute alimentary myositis* has been suggested for this disease. The cause has been considered to be an antivitamin in the flesh of the fish; this inactivates thiamine (i.e., it is an antithiamine). A similar condition occurred in silver foxes on a farm in the United States where the animals had been fed on carp. An antivitamin was demonstrated in the flesh and viscera of the fish (Green *et al.,* 1942).

FRUIT JUICES

Certain natural juices, for example lemon juice, may cause damage to dental enamel (erosion, etching, decalcification) when repeated exposure to their acid content is allowed to take place. Also, highly acid carbonated beverages of low $_p$H may injure the teeth, as in the case of soft drinks (see below).

Acid fruit extracts and soft drinks stored in galvanized iron containers can extract zinc from which acute poisoning has resulted with symptoms such as epigastric pain, vomiting and diarrhea. Apples and other foods cooked in galvanized iron, copper and other types of metal container have also caused poisoning (Locket, 1957; Dewberry, 1959). Sauerkraut and processed foods have in similar manner caused metallic poisoning when stored or cooked in certain containers, especially in the presence of acids. The adventitious metals taken up in food have included antimony, arsenic, cadmium, copper and lead. Specific antidotes for metallic intoxication may be necessary in the treatment of such poisoning, in addition to other measures.

SOFT DRINKS

Certain types of acid soft drinks, also natural fruit squashes such as fresh lemon juice, and acid fruit ices, can produce erosion of the dental enamel from its continued exposure to acids; to some extent this can be prevented by sipping the fluid through a tube and by avoiding swilling the fluid around in the mouth. Sugar, which is present in these preparations, is also incriminated as a cause of dental erosion.

Coca-Cola® and Pepsi-Cola® may contain caffeine 15 mg per bottle of 200 ml, sugar 20 gm, acids and other ingredients (Queries and Minor Notes, 1954). In South Africa the cola drinks have been reported to contain caffeine 15 mg (¼ grain) in six fluid ounces, extract of cola and vanilla, sugar, caramel, salt, essential oils (citrus, spice) orthophosphoric acid and citric acid and carbon dioxide (George, 1959). Methyl alcohol has been added to soft drinks by misguided persons, and has caused blindness and death.

TEA, COFFEE AND RELATED BEVERAGES

Many nonalcoholic beverages are made from plant products containing xanthine derivatives.

Tea

With the exception of water, tea is probably the most consumed beverage in the world. It is more than an aqueous solution of caffeine and tannins.

The principal pharmacological action of infusion of tea is due to the xanthine or purine derivatives, especially caffeine and theophylline. A cup of tea may contain 17 to 110 mg caffeine. Tea is preferable to coffee because it contains less caffeine and volatile oil, and it lacks certain components present in coffee.

Tea contains 1 to 1.5 per cent caffeine, and 10 to 24 per cent tannin, also small quantities of theophylline and theobromine. Volatile or essential oils and certain trace elements, proteins, chlorophyll and various carbohydrates are also present in fresh green tea. Infused tea contains small quantities of riboflavin, nicotinic acid, pantothenic acid and thiamine. An ordinary cup of black tea may contain about 25 μg of riboflavin and 75 μg of pantothenic acid. The highest content of fluorine is in black tea, less in other types. It is sometimes as high as the recommended level in water supplies. Tea, coffee and cocoa are rich in oxalates but very little passes into the prepared beverages.

Although there are many constituents in tea, most only in trace amounts, the pharmacology of tea has been attributed mainly to caffeine which is known to produce definite effects on the central nervous system and other systems of the body. This has been much investigated. The pharmacological effect of tea may possibly be modified by the length of brewing or infusion, which is of some importance. Infusion with boiling water for three minutes extracts most of the caffeine, and the caffeine:tannin ratio is at maximum. Longer brewing adds more tannin but little or no additional caffeine. Reliable information on the effect of tea tannin is limited, but it is stated to be different from that of tannic acid. Some of the other ingredients or characteristics of a cup of tea may be important in determining the effect of tea. A portion of the immediate effect of drinking tea is purely psychological.

It is generally accepted that tea is a relatively harmless beverage in health and disease (Tea: A Symposium, 1955). It has virtues as a soothing agent and for relieving fatigue. It may be useful as a digestive aid and as a mild diuretic. It appears to stimulate gastric motility, increasing the rate of gastric emptying, but it is ordinarily not a potent gastric secretagogue. The tannins of tea may exert a weak astringent action and allay mild irritation in the alimentary canal.

Tea without added milk and sugar has virtually no caloric value and it may therefore be included in all obesity diets. There is no sodium, so that it may be used in salt-restriction diets. Patients with gout and hypertension were once forbidden to have tea and coffee, but this indictment is now regarded as incorrect and based on wrong concepts and facts. There are indeed indications for the use of tea.

Excessive consumption of tea may interfere with digestion and cause gastrointestinal discomfort in some persons, possibly because of the action of tannins or the caffeine content. Caffeine is a stimulant of gastric secretion, and therefore some have recommended that strong tea and coffee be forbidden in patients who have a peptic ulcer.

Some persons develop premature contractions (extrasystoles) after excessive intake of strong tea or coffee. This disturbance may be due to the direct pharmacological action of caffeine, but other causes have been suggested, for example allergy and reflex effect from irritation of the alimentary canal. Large doses of caffeine can produce nervousness, restlessness, insomnia, excitement, tinnitus, tachycardia and extrasystoles.

Irregularity of caffeine intake may lead to "caffeine-withdrawal" headache, for example when a usual morning coffee is not taken. Caffeine relieves this type of headache, but it does not raise the normal pain treshold in the normal person.

Bush Teas. Herbal teas are widely used by many peasant people as flavored drinks and as medicine. They may sometimes be toxic, as for instance the types used in Jamaica that have produced veno-occlusive disease of the liver and cirrhosis, especially in children. The plants that have been incriminated include *Senecio* and *Crotalaria* species, and their hepatotoxic alkaloids are considered in another section (see Bread poisoning). Bush teas, for example, rooibostee, have been much used in South Africa. A list of the plants used, and some information about their constituents is given by Watt and Breyer-Brandwyk (1962). Some of the teas are available on the commercial market. Various medicinal properties have been attributed to them, for example willow tea has been used as a remedy for rheumatism, and violet tea and other teas to improve digestion in stomach disorders. These teas do not contain caffeine and also in most cases no tannin.

Coffee

Coffee beans contain caffeine 1 to 1.5 per cent, tannin, certain acids, fat, sugars and pentosans. The amount of caffeine in a cup of coffee varies with the method of preparation but is approximately 100 to 150 mg. "Instant" coffees contain 52 to 67 mg per cup, and decaffeinated coffee 13 to 35 mg per cup (Drill, 1965). According to *Documenta Geigy-Scientific Tables* (1962) a cup of coffee, 125 ml, contains the following ingredients (approximately) (amount expressed in mg).

Caffeine	95-125
Trigonelline	120
Acetic acid	24
Formic acid	15
Chlorogenic acid	200
Malic acid	23
Citric acid	36
Phenolic acids (other than chlorogenic acid)	60
Nicotinic acid	2

Coffee even in small quantities has unpleasant effects on many people who suffer no such effects from tea. Excessive ingestion of coffee may interfere with digestion and cause gastrointestinal symptoms, possibly because of the action of the volatile (essential) oil. Coffee taken after a meal exerts a carminative action due to the action of the volatile oil (*cf.* liqueurs).

Coffee because of its caffeine content elevates the free fatty acids in the blood serum (Bellet *et al.*, 1965). It also contains a substance which elevates serum lipids in susceptible persons, and such persons may be liable to coronary heart disease, according to Paul *et al.* (1963), and Little *et al.* (1966). On the other hand sugar has been much incriminated (Akinyanju and Yudkin, 1967) (see aso Sugar). Tea, unlike coffee, has no positive correlation with serum lipids. In patients who have maturity-onset diabetes mellitus coffee produces an increase in blood glucose levels (Jankelson *et al.*, 1967), but this has been questioned.

Coffee is frequently adulterated. The most important substance added is chicory which is the root of a wild endive (*Cichorium intybus*). This root is dried, partly caramelized and then added to the coffee in proportions varying from 10 to 80 per cent. It is not regarded as harmful to health, but it may disturb digestion and cause hyperacidity. The plant is poisonous to cattle. Chicory and certain other plants contain the polysaccharide inulin, which is used in the preparation of special breads for diabetics.

One of the substances that has been used as a coffee substitute is *Lathyrus sativus*, the chick pea (*q.v.*) Acorns have been used. Also the roasted pod of *Entada phaseoloides Merr.* (Seabean, Garbee bean, Mackay bean, Sword bean) and the seed alone have been used as a coffee substitute and are stated to be purgative. The seed is edible but is bitter and it contains saponins and other substances.

Kola

The seeds or nuts from various species of cola trees, for example *Cola vera* or *acuminata,* which grows in West Africa, West Indies, Brazil and Java, contain caffeine 1 to 2.5 per cent, some theobromine and other substances not properly identified.

Guarana

This paste is obtained from the seeds of certain plants growing in Brazil, in the Upper Amazon basin. It contains 2.5 to 5 per cent caffeine, "guarana red," and other constituents resembling those of cola and cocoa. It resembles tea and coffee, and in South America the powder is used with water to make a drink.

Maté

Maté, yerba, Paraguay tea or Jesuit tea contains 0.2 to 2 per cent caffeine, tannin, glycosides, essential oils and other substances. It is less astringent than tea and is extensively used as a beverage in South America.

Cocoa

This contains 1.5 to 3 per cent theobromine, also some caffeine and tannin. Because of the high fat content the ingestion of excessive amounts may interfere with digestion and cause gastrointestinal distress.

A bar of chocolate, 100 gm, may contain 50 to 75 mg caffeine and 300 to 400 mg theobromine. The avoidance of cocoa and chocolate lead to improvement of acne in some patients.

ALCOHOLIC BEVERAGES

There is a vast, readily available literature dealing with the general subject of alcohol. Only a few special points will be considered here. A useful volume for reference to details regarding the numerous chemical constituents and pharmacology of alcoholic beverages is the monograph prepared by Leake and Silverman (1966).

Alcohol has a limited value as a food. It is useful in illness and convalescence when appetite is deficient and the assimilation of ordinary food impaired. It improves the appetite by removing worry and anxiety, and by stimulating salivary and gastric secretion. It is an expensive source of energy.

Alcohol leads to wastage of nitrogen and has a high specific dynamic action. It cannot repair waste for which protein is necessary. It contains no vitamins. It cannot be stored. The rate of metabolism is slow, 10 to 15 ml per hour. There is risk of dependence (addiction). There is special risk of severe acute effects when certain drugs including the oral antidiabetic compounds of the sulphonylurea type are being used and possibly also when the inky cap is eaten (see Mushrooms).

Alcohol produces a number of well-known undesirable effects on the gastrointestinal system, the liver and the nervous system, especially in those who indulge in excessive and prolonged drinking. The disturbance in liver function and the development of fatty nutritional cirrhosis (alcoholic cirrhosis) have been much studied; the disorder is due to secondary or conditioned dietary (amino acid and vitamin) deficiency but also to a direct effect of alcohol on the liver. A review of some aspects of this problem is given by Brock and collaborators (1961).

Alcohol induces a rise in serum triglycerides and a decrease in plasma free fatty acids in man and animals, and an increase in liver lipids has been produced in rats (Review, 1964; 1965; 1966). There is strong evidence that the intemperate use of alcohol is detrimental not only to the liver but also to the heart; it has been shown to produce hyperlipidemia and cardiomyopathy (Review, 1966).

Alcohol can produce an excessive amount of iron in the body. This may be due to a large amount of iron in certain alcoholic beverages, as in the case of the South African Bantu (see below). It may be due to increased absorption of ferric iron promoted by alcohol. Another factor is chronic pancreatitis that frequently accompanies liver cirrhosis.

Some wines such as Chianti contain tyramine as much as 25 μg per ml, and beer contains 1 to 4 μg per ml. (Horwitz *et al.,* 1964). This is of practical importance when a patient is receiving antidepressant drugs of the type that inhibit mono-amine oxidase; the tyramine of these drinks becomes absorbed in such amount that hypertension is induced, from the release of adrenaline and noradrenaline, and the results may be serious. A similar phenomenon may occur when a number of amine-containing foods such as cheese and Marmite are taken with these antidepressant drugs.

Safrole is a component of several essential oils, and it was once extensively used in North America as a flavoring agent in

Safrole

root beer. This practice has been discontinued. **Poisoning has** occurred in man, and hepatic tumors have been induced in rats by feeding safrole in the diet (Roe and Lancaster, 1964; Miller and Miller, 1965; see also Flavoring Agents).

Consideration of Some Alcoholic Beverages

Bantu beer is brewed from *Sorghum* seed (Kaffir corn) (millet). It has an alcohol content of 2 to 3 per cent, and it contains factors of the vitamin-B complex. Unfortunately homemade beer and especially illicitly manufactured drink known as "cidivici" may contain harmful additives or contaminants.

It is estimated that in the South African Bantu as much as 50 to 100 mg of iron may be ingested daily in beer alone. This may be compared with the estimation that the general diet in Western countries provides an intake of approximately 10 to 20 mg iron per day. Iron overload results from such excessive intake of iron, the bulk of which is derived from fermented alcoholic beverages and from maize porridge prepared in metal containers (Walker and Arvidsson, 1953; Bothwell *et al.,* 1964; Isaacson, 1966; Uys, 1966; Walker, 1966; van Wyk, 1967). This intake of iron might account for the degree of cytosiderosis found in these subjects in middle age. To what extent this is responsible for cirrhosis is still undecided. Of interest is the fact that the Cape Colored people seldom show siderosis.

A high incidence of symptomatic porphyria occurs in the Colored and Bantu population in South Africa. It appears most likely to be due to ethyl alcohol or some constituent of alcoholic beverages, especially home-brewed liquor and cheap wine. Metabolites of *Aspergillus fumigatus* and other contaminants such as fusel oil have been considered (Hickman *et al.,* 1967). The average fusel oil content of Kaffir beer is high, 227 ppm in comparison with European type beer which contains on average 110 ppm (O'Donovan and Novellie, 1966).

The high and increasing incidence in recent years of esophageal cancer in the Bantu of the Transkei and the Republic of South Africa appears to be associated with the introduction into their way of life of certain new factors which include changes in eating and drinking habits. While eight cases of the disease were reported at hospitals in 1952 there were 360 cases reported in 1960, and the incidence has been increasing. It is considered by some investigators that the most probable cause of the esophageal cancer is some irritant in the "beer" they consume in large quantities. All sorts of foreign substances are added to the "beer," for example aspirin, beetles containing cantharidin, Brasso®, carbide, methylated spirit, shoe polish, wild tobacco and plants. The bark of *Pittosporum viridiflorium Sims* which is bitter and has a peculiar odor is sometimes added to Bantu or Kaffir beer in place of hops. The ripe fruit of *Ximenia americana L.* is also used for making beer; it is purgative. Metal drums and barrels which may contain residual quantities of tar (bitumen), dicophane (DDT), benzene hexachloride (BHC), arsenic and lead (Burrell, 1957; Oettle, 1961) have been used in the preparation of the alcoholic beverages.

The possibility that zinc, present for example in Malawi gin, is involved as a causal agent in esophageal cancer in parts of Central Africa is also being examined (McGlashan, 1967). Also important in the search for the cause of the esophageal cancer are the carcinogenic nitrosamines such as are present in the fungus *Clitocybe suaveolens* and other fungal toxins (see Mushrooms; Peanuts).

It remains to be proved that Bantu beer ever contains aflatoxins. A number of samples of beer from Swaziland (Southern Africa) did not contain *Aspergillus flavus,* but they yielded almost pure cultures of *A. clavatus.* However, clavacin, which is a toxic carcinogenic metabolite produced by certain strains of this fungus, was not detected nor were the beers toxic when fed in dry form to ducklings at the South African Institute for Medical Research.

Intoxicating beverages of many kinds other than the abovementioned Bantu beer types are prepared from a variety of sugary substances. In places where the grape or grain is not present, fruit juices or the sap of plants have been used, for example the toddy palm, honey and sugar of milk used by the Tartar tribes. The following list indicates some of the plants that have been utilized in African countries and elsewhere for the preparation of fermented liquors; details about these plants and others are given by Watt and Breyer-Brandwyk (1962). The sap and in some instances the fruit of certain palm plants are used to make fermented beverages, palm wines, as in the case of the following: surra from *Borassus flabellifer L.* var. *aethiopum Warb.;* toddy and temba from coconut palm *Cocos nucifera L.*, from which beverage arrack is obtained by distillation; a palm wine, malovu, from *Elaeis guineensis* Jacq.; a kind of rum from *Hyphaene coriaca Gaertn.* and *Hyphaene crinita Gaertn.;* other palm wines, from *Hyphaene ventricosa Kirk., Phoenix reclinata Jacq., Raphia pedunculata Beauv.* and *Raphia vinifera P. Beauv.* Intoxicating drinks are also made from the fruit of *Annona muricata L.* (soursop), Ficus *gnaphalocarpa Steud. ex A. Rich.* (a wild fig), *Ximenia americana L.* (mountain plum, seaside plum, sourplum, wild lime, wild plum, yellow plum), and from various *Opuntia* (prickly pear) species. The yellow plumlike fruit of *Sclerocarya caffra* Sond. (marula or cider tree) is eaten by human beings, baboons, monkeys and elephants, and it is used to make an intoxicating beverage, for example a beer known as *ukanya.* Even the consumption of a large quantity of this fruit by elephants can cause them to become intoxicated. The fruit of *Kigelia aethiopica Decne* (African sausage tree, cucumber tree) is added to beer in Tanzania to increase its strength presumably by increased fermentation and the formation of amyl alcohol. The juice of *Agave americana L.* (American agave; American aloe; century plant), which contains a sugar known as agavose, is used in Mexico to make a fermented intoxicating drink called pulque.

BIBLIOGRAPHY

Aas, K.: Studies of hypersensitivity to fish. A clinical study. *Int Arch Allerg, 29*:346, 1966.

Ahlumalia, H. S., and Duguid, J. B.: Malignant tumours in Malaya. *Brit J Cancer, 20*:12, 1966.

Akinyanju, P., and Yudkin, J.: Effect of coffee and tea on serum lipids in the rat. *Nature, 214*:426, 1967.

Al-Nagdy, S.; Miller, D. S.; Qureshi, R. U., and Yudkin, J.: Metabolic differences between starch and sucrose. *Nature, 209*:81, 1966.

Altman, P. L., and Dittmer, D. S.: *Biological Data Book.* Washington, D. C., Fed Amer Soc Exp Biol, 1964.

Ambrose, A. M.: Naturally occurring antienzymes (inhibitors); see National Academy of Sciences, 1966.

Anderson, W.; Burton, L. K., and Crookall, J. O.: Radiostrontium and radiocaesium in milk during 1959. *Nature, 187*:108, 1960.

Annotation: Paralysis in Morocco. *Brit Med J, 1*:630, 1960.

Annotation: Peanuts and haemophilia. *Brit Med J, 1*:630, 1960.

Annotation: Radioactive iodine in milk. *Brit Med J, 2*:1275, 1961.

Annotation (a): Toxic product in ground-nuts. *Brit Med J, 1*:309, 1962.

Annotation (b): Toxic product in ground-nuts. *Brit Med J, 2*:534, 1962.

Annotation: The cheese reaction. *Lancet, 1*:540, 1964.

Annotation: Antibodies and alimentary disease. *Brit Med J, 2*:328, 1964.

Annotation: Oesophageal cancer. *Brit Med J, 2*:718, 1966.

Antia, F. P.: *Clinical Dietetics and Nutrition.* London, New York, Oxford U. P., 1966.

Any Questions: Radioactive substances in breast milk. *Brit Med J, 2*:1375, 1961.

Any Questions: Nitrates in drinking-water. *Brit Med J, 2*:95, 1965.

Arena, J. M.: *Poisoning.* Springfield, Ill., Thomas, 1963.

Arnold, J. R., and Martell, E. A.: The circulation of radioactive isotopes. *Sci Amer, 201*:85, 1959.

Arnott, W. M.: A problem in tropical cardiology. *Brit Med J, 2*:1273, 1959.

Asano, M., and Itoh, M.: Salivary poison of a marine gastropod, *Neptunea arthritica* Bernardi, and the seasonal variation of its toxicity. *Ann N Y Acad Sci, 90*:674, 1960.

149

ASATOOR, A. M.; LEVI, A. J., and MILNE, M. D.: Tranylcypromine and cheese. *Lancet,* 2:733, 1963.

ASHLEY, L. M.; HALVER, J. E., and WOGAN, G. N.: Hepatoma and aflatoxicosis in trout. *Fed Proc,* 23:105, 1964.

ASPLIN, F. D., and CARNAGHAN, R. B. A.: The toxicity of certain groundnut meals for poultry with special reference to their effect on ducklings and chickens. *Vet Rec,* 73:1215, 1961.

BARNES, J. M.: Suggestions for the provision of advice and research on toxicological problems in New Zealand. *New Zeal Med J,* 65:122, 1966.

BELLET, S.; KERSCHBAUM, A., and ASPE, J.: The effect of caffeine on free fatty acids. *Arch Intern Med,* 116:750, 1965.

BERGEN, S. S., and ROELS, O. A.: Hypervitaminosis A. *Amer J Clin Nutr,* 16:265, 1965.

BEWLEY, T. H.: Acute water-intoxication from compulsive water-drinking. *Brit Med J,* 2:864, 1964.

BINGLE, J. P., and LENNARD-JONES, J. E.: Some factors in the assessment of gastric antisecretory drugs by a sampling technique. *Gut,* 1:337, 1960.

BIRD, H. R.: Additives and residues in foods of animal origin. *Amer J Clin Nutr,* 9:260, 1961.

BIRD, P. M.: Radionuclides in foods. *Canad Med Ass J,* 94:590, 1966.

BISORDI, M. V.: Peanut flour in haemophilia. *Lancet,* 2:476, 1964.

BLACKWELL, B., and MABBITT, L. A.: Tyramine in cheese related to hypertensive crises after monoamine-oxidase inhibition. *Lancet,* 1:938, 1965.

BLACKWELL, B.; MARLEY, E., and MABBITT, L. A.: Effects of yeast extract after monoamine-oxidase inhibition. *Lancet,* 1:940, 1965.

BLOCK, S. S.; STEPHENS, R. L.; BARRETO, A., and MURRILL, W. A.: Chemical identification of the *Amanita* toxin in mushrooms. *Science,* 121:505, 1955.

BLOOD, F. R., and RUDOLPH, G. G.: Some naturally occurring stimulants and depressants; see National Academy of Sciences, 1966.

BONGIRWAR, D. R., and KUMTA, U. S.: Preservation of cheese with combined use of gamma-rays and sorbic acid. *Int J Appl Radiat,* 18:133, 1967.

BONSER, G. M.: Factors concerned in the location of human and experimental tumours. *Brit Med J,* 1:655, 1967.

BOTHWELL, T. H.; SEFTEL, H.; JACOBS, P.; TORRANCE, J. D., and BAUMSLAG, N.; Iron overload in Bantu subjects: Studies on the availability of iron in Bantu beer. *Amer J Clin Nutr,* 14:47, 1964.

BOUDREAUX, H. B., and FRAMPTON, V.: A peanut factor for haemostasis in haemophilia. *Nature,* 185:469, 1960.

BOYD, W. C.: The lectins: their present status. *Vox Sang,* 8:1, 1963.

BRANDENBERGER, H., and BADER, H.: Uber den Einbau von Trichloräthylen in Inhaltsstoffe des Kaffees bei dessen Decoffeinierung. *Helv Chim Acta,* 50:463, 1967.

BRAS, G.; JELLIFFE, D. B., and STUART, K. L.: Veno-occlusive disease of liver with nonportal type of cirrhosis, occurring in Jamaica. *Arch Path, 57*:285, 1954.

BRAS, G.; BERRY, D. M., and GYÖRGY, P.: Plants as aetiological factor in veno-occlusive disease of the liver. *Lancet, 1*:960, 1957.

BRINK, A. J.; LEWIS, C. M., and WEBER, H. W.: Myocardiopathy in *Argemone Mexicana* poisoning. *S Afr Med J, 39*:108, 1965.

BROCK, J. F.: *Recent Advances in Human Nutrition.* London, Churchill, 1961.

BROCKINGTON, I. F.; OLSEN, E. G. J., and GOODWIN, J. F.: Endomyocardial fibrosis in Europeans resident in tropical Africa. *Lancet, 1*:583, 1967.

BROOKES, L. G.: Use of synthetic sweetening agents. *Chem Drug, 183*:421, 1965.

BROWN, J. M. M., and ABRAMS, L.: Biochemical studies on aflatoxicosis. *Onderstepoort J Vet Res, 32*:119, 1965.

BROWN, J. M. M., and DE WET, P. J.: A survey of the occurrence of potentially harmful amounts of selenium in the vegetation of the Karoo. *Onderstepoort J Vet Res 34*:161, 1967.

BROWN, W. H., and FELAUER, E. E.: A new fatty acid from royal jelly. *Nature, 190*:88, 1961.

BRUCE, D. W.: Carcinoid tumours and pineapples. *J Pharm Pharmacol, 13*:256, 1961.

BURRELL, R. J. W.: Oesophageal cancer in the Bantu. *S Afr Med J, 31*:401, 1957.

BURRELL, R. J. W.: Cancer of the gullet among reserve-domiciled Bantu. *Leech, 29*:146, 1959.

BURRELL, R. J. W.: Esophageal cancer among Bantu in the Transkei. *J Nat Cancer Inst, 29*:495, 1962.

BURRELL, R. J. W.; ROACH, W. A., and SHADWELL, A.: Esophageal cancer in the Bantu of the Transkei associated with mineral deficiency in garden plants. *J Nat Cancer Inst, 36*:201, 1966.

BUTLER, W. H.: Acute toxicity of aflatoxin B_1 in rats. *Brit J Cancer, 18*:756, 1964.

BUTLER, W. H., and CLIFFORD, J. I.: Extraction of aflatoxin from rat liver. *Nature, 206*:1045, 1965.

BUTLER, W. H.: Early hepatic parenchymal changes induced by aflatoxin B_1. *Amer J. Path, 49*:113, 1966.

BUTLER, W. H.: Acute toxicity of aflatoxin B_1 in guinea-pigs. *J Path Bact 91*:277, 1966.

BUTLER, W. H., and BARNES, J. M.: Carcinoma of the glandular stomach in rats given diets containing aflatoxin. *Nature, 209*:90, 1966.

BUTLER, W. H., and WIGGLESWORTH, J. S.: The effects of aflatoxin B_1 on the pregnant rat. *Brit J Exp Path, 47*:242, 1966.

CALVIN, M. E.; KNEPPER, R., and ROBERTSON, W. O.: Salt poisoning. *New Eng J Med, 270*:625, 1964.

CARNAGHAN, R. B. A.: Hepatic tumours in ducks fed a low level of toxic groundnut meal. *Nature, 208*:308, 1965.

CARR, W. R., and MERCER, E. R.: Strontium-90 in human diet in Northern and Southern Rhodesia. *Cent Afr J Med, 8*:183, 1962.

CHAPMAN, R. A., and MORRISON, A. B.: Regulatory agencies and food safety. *Canad Med Ass J, 94*:609, 1966.

CHEN, K. K.; ANDERSON, R. C.; McCOWEN, M. C., and HARRIS, P. N.: Pharmacologic action of hypoglycin A and B. *J Pharm, 121*:272, 1957.

CHEN, K. K.; FLEMING, W. J., and LIN, T. M.: Action of hypoglycin A on blood sugar, gastric secretion, and adipose tissue. *J Pharm, 134*:435, 1961.

CHEUNG, K. K., and SIM, G. A.: Aflatoxin G_1: Direct determination of the structure by the method of isomorphous replacement. *Nature, 201*:1185, 1964.

CHRISTENSEN, G. M.: Identification of sugars in royal jelly. *Nature, 195*:74, 1962.

CLEAVE, T. L., and CAMPBELL, G. D.: *Diabetes, Coronary Thrombosis, and Saccharine Disease.* Bristol, John Wright & Sons, 1966.

CLEMENTS, F. W.: Naturally occurring goitrogens. *Brit Med Bull, 16*:133, 1960.

CLIFFORD, J. I., and REES, K. R.: Aflatoxin: a site of action in the rat liver cell. *Nature, 209*:312, 1966.

COADY, A.: Aflatoxin. *Brit Med J, 1*:1510, 1964.

COLHOUN, E. H., and SMITH, M. V.: Neurohormonal properties of royal jelly. *Nature, 188*:854, 1960.

COMAR, C. L.: Natural radioactivity in the biosphere and foodstuffs; see National Academy of Science, 1966.

Committee on Nutrition: Report of the Committee on Nutrition. *Pediatrics. 31*:329, 1963.

CRAWFORD, M. A.: Endomyocardial fibrosis and carcinoidosis. a common denominator? *Amer Heart J, 66*:273, 1963.

CROSBY, D. G.: Natural cholinesterase inhibitors in food; see National Academy of Science, 1966.

CROUT, J. R., and SJOERDSMA, A.: The clinical and laboratory significance of serotonin and catechol amines in bananas. *New Eng J Med, 261*:23, 1959.

CULVENOR, C. C. J.; DANN, A. T., and DICK, A. T.: Alkylation as the mechanism by which the hepatotoxic pyrrolizidine alkaloids act on cell nuclei. *Nature, 195*:570, 1962.

DAHL, L. K.: Salt, fat and hypertension: The Japanese experience. *Nutr Rev, 18*:97, 1960.

DAVIDSON, C. S.: Plants and fungi as hepatotoxins. *Nutr Rev, 22:*97, 1964.

DAVIDSON, S., and PASSMORE, R: *Human Nutrition and Dietetics.* Edinburgh and London, Livingstone, 1966.

DAY, P. L.: The food and drug administration faces new responsibilities. *Nutr Rev, 18:*1, 1960.

DAYAN, A. D.: A note on royal jelly; a critical evaluation. *J Pharm Pharmacol, 12:*377, 1960.

DEAN, G.: The Turkish epidemic of porphyria. *S Afr Med J, 35:*509, 1961.

DEICHMANN, W. B., and GERARDE, H. W.: *Symptomatology and Therapy of Toxicological Emergencies.* New York, London, Academic, 1964.

DE IONGH, H.; VLES, R. O., and VAN PELT, J. G.: Milk of mammals fed on aflatoxin-containing diet. *Nature, 202:*466, 1964.

DE MATTEIS, F.; PRIOR, B. E., and RIMINGTON, C.: Nervous and biochemical disturbances following hexachlorobenzene intoxication. *Nature, 191:*363, 1961.

Department of Nutrition: Endemic goitre in South Africa. Union of South Africa, 1955.

DE RECONDO, A. M.; FRAYSSINET, C.; LAFARGE, C., and LE BRETON, E.: Effect of aflatoxin B_1 on DNA metabolism in regenerating rat liver. *Pharm Tox, Excerpta Med,* (abstract 60), *20:*8, 1967.

DEWBERRY, E. B.: *Food Poisoning,* 4th ed. London, Leonard Hill.

DE WIT, J. P.; PURCHASE, I. F. H.; VAN DER WALT, J. P., and VORSTER, L. J.: Mycotoxins in food—Recent advances in South Africa. *S Afr Med J, 40:*1097, 1966.

DICKENS, F., and JONES, H. E. H.: The carcinogenic action of aflatoxin after its subcutaneous injection in the rat. *Brit J Cancer, 17:*691: 1963.

DICKENS, F.: Carcinogenic lactones and related substances. *Brit Med Bull, 20:*96, 1964.

DIENER, U. L.; DAVIS, N. D.; SALMON, W. D., and PRICKETT, C. O.: Toxin-producing *Aspergillus* isolated from domestic peanuts. *Science, 142:*1491, 1963.

Dispensatory of the U. S., 25th ed. Philadelphia, Montreal, Lippincott, 1955.

DIXIT, P. K., and PATEL, N. G.: Insulin-like activity in larval foods of the honeybee. *Nature, 202:*189, 1964.

Documenta Geigy-Scientific Tables, 6th ed. Basle, J. R. Geigy, S.A., 1962.

DOLL, R.; PRICE, A. V.; PYGOTT, F., and SANDERSON, P. H.: Continuous intra-gastric milk drip in treatment of uncomplicated gastric ulcer. *Lancet, 1:*70, 1956.

DOLL, R.: Medical treatment of gastric ulcer. *Scot Med J, 9:*183, 1964.

DREISBACH, R. H.: *Handbook of Poisoning,* 5th ed. Los Altos, Calif., Lange, 1966.

DRILL, V.: *Pharmacology in Medicine,* 3rd ed. New York, McGraw, 1965.

DUGAN, S., and HOLLIDAY, M. A.: Water intoxication in two infants following the voluntary ingestion of excessive fluids. *Pediatrics, 39*:418, 1967.

DUNACHIE, J. F., and FLETCHER, W. W.: Effect of some insecticides on the hatching rate of hens' eggs. *Nature, 212*:1062, 1966.

DUNGAL, N.: The special problem of stomach cancer in Iceland. *JAMA, 178*:789, 1961.

DYBING, O., and ERICHSEN, S.: Liver changes in rats after administration of *Senecio aquaticus. Acta Path Microbiol Scand, 47*:1, 1959.

EAGLE, E.: Gossypol; see National Academy of Sciences, 1966.

EARLE, K. V.: Toxic effects of *Hippomane mancinella. Trans Roy Soc Trop Med Hyg, 32*:363, 1938.

EGAN, H.; GOULDING, R.; ROBURN, J., and TATTON, J. O.: Organo-chlorine pesticide residues in human fat and human milk. *Brit Med J, 2*:66, 1965.

ELKINGTON, S. G.; McBRIEN, D. J., and SPENCER, H.: Hepatoma in cirrhosis. *Brit Med J, 2*:1501, 1963.

ELLIOT, W.; HALL, M.; KERR, D. N. S.; ROLLAND, C. F.; SMART, G. A., and SWINNEY, J.: Mushroom poisoning. *Lancet, 2*:630, 1961.

EVANS, M. H.: Cause of death in experimental paralytic shellfish poisoning. *Brit J Exp Path, 46*:245, 1965.

Extra Pharmacopoeia, 25th ed. London, Pharmaceutical Press, 1967.

FANGE, R.: The salivary gland of *Neptunea antiqua. Ann N Y Acad Sci, 90*:689, 1960.

FASSETT, D. W.: Nitrates and nitrites; see National Academy of Sciences, 1966.

FASSETT, D. W.: Oxalates, see National Academy of Sciences, 1966.

FEIGEN, G. A.; SANZ, E., and ALENDER, C. B.: Studies on the mode of action of sea urchin toxin. *Toxicon, 4*:161, 1966.

FENG, P. C., and KEAN, E. A.: Influence of diet on the acute toxicity of hypoglycin-A in rats. *Brit J Nutr, 9*:368, 1955.

FEUELL, A. J.: Toxic factors of mould origin. *Canad Med Ass J, 94*:574, 1966.

FINBERG, L.; KILEY, J., and LUTTRELL, C. N.: Mass accidental salt poisoning in infancy. *JAMA, 184*:187, 1963.

FINGERMAN, M.; FORESTER, R. H., and STOVER, J. H.: Action of shellfish poison on peripheral nerve and skeletal muscle. *Proc Soc Exp Biol Med, 84*:643, 1953.

FISHER, H.; SILLER, W. G., and GRIMINGER, P.: The retardation by pectin of cholesterol-induced atherosclerosis in the fowl. *J Atheroscl Res, 6*:292, 1966.

FISTEIN, B.: Toxic hypoglycaemia. *W Indian Med J, 9*:62, 1960.

FITZHUGH, O. G.: Problems related to the use of pesticides. *Canad Med Ass J, 94*:598, 1966.

FORGACS, J.: Types of mycotoxicity occurring in feeds and foods. *Food Tech,* 20:46, 1966.

FOY, J. M., and PARRATT, J. R.: A note on the presence of noradrenaline and 5-hydroxytryptamine in plantain (*Musa sapientum,* var. *paradisiaca*). *J Pharm Pharmacol, 12*:360, 1960.

FOY, J. M., and PARRATT, J .R.: 5-Hydroxytryptamine in pineapples. *J Pharm Pharmacol, 13*:382, 1961.

FOY, H.; GILLMAN, T.; KONDI, A., and PRESTON, J. K.: Hepatic injuries in riboflavine and pyridoxine deficient baboons—Possible relations to aflatoxin induced hepatic cirrhosis and carcinoma in Africans. *Nature, 212*:150, 1966.

FROST, D. V.: Arsenic and selenium in relation to the Food Additive Law of 1958. *Nutr Rev, 18*:129, 1960.

FUHRMAN, F. A.: Tetrodotoxin. *Sci Amer, 217*:60, 1967.

GABBAI, LISBONNE, and POURQUIERS: Ergot poisoning at Pont St. Esprit. *Brit Med J, 2*:650, 1951.

GARROD, L. P.: Antibiotics in food. *Practitioner, 195*:36, 1965.

GEORGE, E.: Soft drinks. *Lancet, 1*:836, 1959.

GLEASON, M. N.; GOSSELIN, R. E., and HODGE, H. C.: *Clinical Toxicology of Commercial Products.* Baltimore, Williams & Wilkins, 1963.

GODFREY, C. M.: An epidemic of triorthocresylphosphate poisoning. *Canad Med Ass J, 85*:689, 1961.

GOLDBLITH, S. A.: Possible application to food of ionizing and non-ionizing radiations. *J Amer Diet Ass, 51*:233, 1967.

GOODMAN, L. S., and GILMAN, A.: *The Pharmacological Basis of Therapeutics,* 3rd ed. New York, Macmillan, 1965.

GREEN, R. C.: Nutmeg poisoning. *JAMA, 171*:1342, 1959.

GREEN, R. G.; CARLSON, W. E., and EVANS, C. A.: The inactivation of vitamin B₁ in diets containing whole fish. *J Nutr, 23*:165, 1942.

GREER, M. A.: Goitrogenic substances in food. *Amer J Clin Nutr, 5*:440, 1957.

GROSS, E. G.; DEXTER, J. D., and ROTH, R. G.: Hypokalemic myopathy with myoglobinuria associated with licorice ingestion. *New Eng J Med, 274*: 602, 1966.

HALBERT, E., and WEEDEN, D. G.: Lipase activity in black pepper. *Nature, 212*:1603, 1966.

HALL, R. L.: Toxicants occurring naturally in spices and flavors; see National Academy of Sciences, 1966.

HALSTEAD, B. W.: Fish poisoning—their diagnosis, pharmacology, and treatment. *Clin Pharm Ther, 5*:615, 1964.

HALSTEAD, B. W.: *Poisonous and Venomous Marine Animals of the World* (Vol. 1—*Invertebrates*). Washington, D. C., U.S. Govt. Printing Office, 1965.

HANNINGTON, E.:   Preliminary report on tyramine headache. *Brit Med J,* *1*:550, 1967.

HARINGTON, J. S.:   Potential dangers relating to laboratory work on the Aspergilli and their toxins. *S Afr Med J, 41*:282, 1967.

HARMAN, D.:   Atherosclerosis: Possible ill-effects of the use of highly unsaturated fats to lower serum-cholesterol levels. *Lancet 2*:1116, 1957.

HAVRE, G. N.; HELGEBOSTAD, A., and ENDER, F.:   Iron resorption in fish-induced anaemia in mink. *Nature, 215*:187, 1967.

Hawk's Physiological Chemistry, 14th ed. New York, McGraw, 1965.

HEINER, D. C.; WILSON, J. F., and LAHEY, M. E.:   Sensitivity to cow's milk. *JAMA, 189*:563, 1964.

HICKMAN, R.; SAUNDERS, S. J., and EALES, L.:   Treatment of symptomatic porphyria by venesection. *S Afr Med J, 41*:456, 1967.

HILL, K. R.:   The world-wide distribution of Seneciosis in man and animals. *Proc. Roy Soc Med, 53*:281, 1960.

HILL, K. R.:   Comment on the histological appearances in liver biopsies and post-mortem appearances. *Vet Rec, 75*:493, 1963.

HODGE, J. V.; NYE, E. R., and EMERSON, G. W.:   Monoamine-oxidase inhibitors, broad beans, and hypertension. *Lancet, 1*:1108, 1964.

HODGES, R. E.:   The toxicity of pesticides and their residues in food. *Nutr Rev, 23*:225, 1965.

HOLZAPFEL, C. W., PURCHASE, I. F. H.; STEYN, P. S., and GOUWS, L.:   The toxicity and chemical assay of sterigmatocystin, a carcinogenic mycotoxin, and its isolation from two new fungal sources. *S Afr Med J, 40*: 1100, 1966.

HOONG, LOO, Y., and RITMAN, P.:   Phenylketonuria and vitamin B₆ function. *Nature, 213*:914, 1967.

HORWITZ, D.; LOWENBERG, W.; ENGELMAN, K., and SJOERDSMA, A.:   Monoamine oxidase inhibitors, tyramine, and cheese. *JAMA, 188*:1108, 1964.

HSIA, D. Y.:   Clinical variants of galactosemia. *Metabolism, 16*:419, 1967.

HUDSON, T. G. F.:   *Vanadium, Toxicology and Biological Significance.* Amsterdam, London, New York, Elsevier, 1964.

HUEPER, W. C.:   Carcinogens in the human environment. *Arch Path, 71*:355, 1961.

HUEPER, W. C.:   Environmental and occupational cancer hazards. *Clin Pharmacol Ther, 3*:776, 1962.

HUISMAN, F., and VASBINDER, H.:   A case of food poisoning caused by Chinese wood oil (Tung oil). *Nutr Abstr Rev, 32*:552, 1962.

HVINDEN, T., and LILLEGRAVEN, A.:   Caesium-137 and Strontium-90 in Norwegian milk, 1960-64. *Nature, 210*:580, 1966.

ISAACSON, C.:   Some aspects of pathology in the South African Bantu. *Med Proc, 12*:355, 1966.

JANKELSON, O. M.; BEASER, S. B.; HOWARD, F. M., and MAYER, J.:   Effect of coffee on glucose tolerance and circulating insulin in men with maturity-onset diabetes. *Lancet, 1*:527, 1967.

JONES, W. O.: *Manioc in Africa.* Stanford, Calif, 1959.

KAO, C. Y.: Tetrodotoxin, saxitoxin and their significance in the study of excitation phenomena. *Pharmacol Rev, 18*:997, 1966.

KAO, C. Y.; SUZUKI, T.; KLEINHAUS, A. L., and SIEGMAN, M. J.: Vasomotor and respiratory depressant action of tetrodotoxin and saxitoxin. *Arch Int Pharmacodyn, 165*:438, 1967.

KEELE, C. A., and ARMSTRONG, D.: *Substances Producing Pain and Itch.* London, Edward Arnold, 1964.

KEISER, H. R., and SJOERDSMA, A.: Studies on beta-aminopropionitrile in patients with scleroderma. *Clin Pharmacol Ther, 8*:593, 1967.

KEKWICK, A.: Some problems of food additives. *Practitioner, 195*:32, 1965.

KELLAWAY, C. H.: Mussel poisoning. *Med J Aust, 1*:399, 1935 (a).

KELLAWAY, C. H.: Action of mussel poison on nervous system. *Aust J Exp Biol Med Sci, 13*:79, 1935 (b).

KINGSBURY, J. M.: *Poisonous Plants of the United States and Canada.* Englewood Cliffs, N. J., Prentice-Hall, 1964.

KNAPP, H. A.: Iodine-131 in fresh milk and human thyroids following a single deposition of nuclear test fall-out. *Nature, 202*:534, 1964.

KNOTEK, Z., and SCHMIDT, P.: Pathogenesis, incidence, and possibilities of preventing alimentary nitrate methemoglobinemia in infants. *Pediatrics, 34*:78, 1964.

KNOWLES, J. A.: Excretion of drugs in milk—a review. *J Pediat, 66*:1068, 1965.

KRAYBILL, H. F.: Carcinogenesis associated with foods, food additives, food degradation products, and related dietary factors. *Clin Pharmacol Ther, 4*:73, 1963.

KRAYBILL, H. F., and SHIMKIN, M. B.: Carcinogenesis related to foods contaminated by processing and fungal metabolites. *Advances Cancer Res, 8*:191, 1964.

KRAYBILL, H. F., and WHITEHAIR, L. A.: Toxicological safety of irradiated foods. *Ann Rev. Pharm, 7*:357, 1967.

KUN, E., and HORVATH, I.: The influence of oral saccharin on blood sugar. *Proc Soc Exp Biol Med, 66*:175, 1947.

KUO, P. T., and BASSETT, D. R.: Dietary sugar in the production of hyperglyceridemia. *Ann Intern Med, 62*:1199, 1965.

Laboratory report: Natural principles specific to garlic. *Triangle, 1*:51, 1953.

LAQUEUR, G. L.; MICKELSON, O.; WHITING, M. G., and KURLAND, L. T.: Carcinogenic properties of nuts from *Cycas circinalis* L. indigenous to Guam. *J Nat Cancer Inst, 31*:919, 1963.

LAQUEUR, G. L.: Carcinogenic effects of cycad meal and cycasin, methylazomethanol glycoside, in rats and effects of cycasin in germfree rats. *Fed Proc, 23*:1386, 1964.

LEA, C. H.: Problems arising from the use of chemicals in food. *Chem Industr, 71*:178, 1952.

Leading Article. Carcinogen in groundnuts. *Brit Med J, 2*:204, 1964.

Leading Article: Pesticides in the body. *Brit Med J, 2*:62, 1965.

LEAKE, C., and SILVERMAN, M.: *Alcoholic Beverages in Clinical Medicine.* Chicago, Year Bk, 1966.

LEGATOR, M.: Biological effects of aflatoxin in cell culture. *Bact Rev, 30*: 471, 1966.

LENNARD-JONES, J. E.: Measurement of gastric secretion and acidity. *Proc Roy Soc Med, 59* (Suppl) :1, 1966.

LEPKOVSKY, S.: Antivitamins in foods; see National Academy of Sciences, 1966.

LEVENE, C. I.: Collagen in experimental osteolathyrism. *Fed Proc, 22*:1386, 1963.

LIENER, I. E.: Lathyrogens in foods; see National Academy of Sciences, 1966.

LIJINSKY, W., and BUTLER, W. H.: Purification and toxicity of aflatoxin G_1. *Proc Soc Exp Biol Med, 123*:151, 1966.

LIST, P. H., and REITH, H.: Der Faltentintling, *Coprinus atramentarius* Bull., und seine dem Tetraäthylthiuramdisulfid ähnliche Wirkung. *Arzneimittelforschung, 10*:34, 1960.

LITTLE, J. A.; SHANOFF, H. M.; CSIMA, A., and YANO, R.: Coffee and serum-lipids in coronary heart-disease. *Lancet, 1*:732, 1966.

LOCKET, S.: *Clinical Toxicology.* London, Henry Kimpton, 1957.

LOOSMORE, R. M., and HARDING, J. D. J.: A toxic factor in Brazilian groundnut causing liver damage in pigs. *Vet Rec, 73*:1362, 1961.

MACDONALD, I.: Dietary carbohydrates and lipid metabolism. *Nutr Rev, 22*:257, 1964.

MADSHUS, K., and BAARLI, J.: Radiocaesium and potassium-40 in Norwegian-produced milk. *Nature, 186*:527, 1960.

MAGEE, P. N., and SCHOENTAL, R.: Carcinogenesis by nitroso compounds. *Brit Med Bull, 20*:102, 1964.

MAINWARING, D., and KEIDAN, S. E.: Peanut flour in haemophilia. *Lancet, 2*:647, 1964.

MANN, T .P.; WILSON, K. M., and CLAYTON, B. E.: A deficiency state arising in infants on synthetic foods. *Arch Dis Child, 40*:364, 1965.

MANSMANN, H. C.: Foods as antigens and allergens; see National Academy of Sciences, 1966.

MANSON-BAHR, P. H.: *Manson's Tropical Diseases.* London, Bailliere, Tindall and Cox, 1966.

MARKO, P.; PECHAN, I., and VITTEK, J.: Some phosphorous compounds in royal jelly. *Nature, 202*:188, 1964.

MARSHALL, P. B.: Catechols and tryptamines in the "matoke" banana (*Musa paradisiaca*). *J Pharm Pharmacol, 11*:639, 1959.

McGLASHAN, N. D.: Zinc and oesophageal cancer. *Lancet, 1*:578, 1967.

McNeill, K. G., and Trojan, O. A. D.: Caesium-137 in Toronto milk during 1959. *Nature, 186*:399, 1960.

Meneely, G. R.: Toxic effects of dietary sodium chloride and the protective effect of potassium; see National Academy of Sciences, 1966.

Meyer, K. F.; Sommer, H., and Schoenholz, P.: Mussel poisoning. *J Prevent Med, 2*:365, 1928.

Meyler, L.: *Side Effects of Drugs.* Amsterdam, New York, London; Excerpta Medica Foundation. 1966, vol. V.

Mickelsen, O., and Yang, M. G.: Naturally occurring toxicants in foods. *Fed Proc, 25*:104, 1966.

Miller, D. S., Stirling, J. L., and Yudkin, J.: Effect of ingestion of milk on concentrations of blood alcohol. *Nature, 212*:1051, 1966.

Miller, J. A.: Tumorigenic and carcinogenic products; see National Academy of Sciences, 1966.

Miller, J. A., and Miller, E. C.: Natural and synthetic chemical carcinogens in the etiology of cancer. *Cancer Res, 25*:1292, 1965.

Miller, E. C., and Miller, J. A.: Mechanisms of chemical carcinogenesis. *Pharmacol Rev, 18*:805, 1966.

Ministry of Agriculture, Fisheries and Food: Memorandum on Procedures for Submission on Food Additives and on Methods of Testing. London, H. M. Stationery Office, 1965.

Moffie, D., and Haneveld, G. T.: Ciguatera, fish poisoning in the Caribbean area. *Nederl T Geneesk, 108*:988, 1964.

Molhuysen, J. A.; Gerbrandy, J.; de Vries, L. A., and de Jong, J. C.; Lenstra, J. B.; Turner, K. P., and Borst, J. G. G.: A liquorice extract with deoxycortone-like action. *Lancet, 2*:381, 1950.

Molnar, G. D.; Berge, K. G.; Rosevear, J. W.; McGuckin, W. F., and Achor, R. W. P.: The effect of nicotinic acid in diabetes mellitus. *Metabolism, 13*:181, 1964.

Molnar, J., and György, L.: Pulmonary hypertensive and other haemodynamic effects of capsaicin in the cat. *Eur J Pharm, 1*:86, 1967.

Montgomery, R. D.: The medicinal significance of cyanogen in plant foodstuffs. *Amer J Clin Nutr, 17*:103, 1965.

Mosher, H. S.; Fuhrman, F. A.; Buckwals, H. D., and Fischer, H. G.: Tarichatoxin-tetrodotoxin: A potent neurotoxin. *Science, 144*:1100, 1964.

Murphy, K. J.: Bilateral renal calculi and aminoaciduria after excessive intake of Worcestershire sauce. *Lancet, 2*:401, 1967.

Murtha, E. F.: Pharmacological study of poisons from shellfish and puffer fish. *Ann N Y Acad Sci, 90*:820, 1960.

National Academy of Sciences—National Research Council: Chemicals Used in Food Processing. Publication 1274. Washington, D. C., 1965.

National Academy of Sciences—National Research Council. Food Protection
Committee: Toxicants Occurring Naturally in Foods. Publication 1354.
Washington, D. C., 1966.

NEAME, P. B., and PILLAY, V. K. G.: Spontaneous hypoglycaemia, hepatic
and renal necrosis following the intake of herbal medicines. *S Afr Med
J, 38*:729, 1964.

NICHOLLS, L.; SINCLAIR, H. M., and JELLIFFE, D. B.: *Tropical Nutrition and
Dietetics,* 4th ed. London, Bailliere, Tindall and Cox, 1961.

NIEMAN, C.: Licorice. *Advances in Food Research.* New York, Academic,
1957, vol. VII.

Ninth Report of FAO/WHO Expert Committee on Food Additives. *WHO
Tech Rep Ser.* No. 339, 1966.

Note: Poisoning by pine-apples. *S Afr J Sci, 9*:111, 1912.

NUESSLE, W. F.; NORMAN, F. C., and MILLER, H. E.: Pickled herring and
tranylcypromine reaction. *JAMA, 192*:726, 1965.

O'DONOVAN, and NOVELLIE, L.: Kaffircorn malting and brewing studies. XV.
The fusel oils of Kaffir beer. *J Sci Food Agric, 17*:362, 1966.

OETTLE, A. G.: Cancer and environmental influences: Some observations on
its geographical pathology. *Leech, 31*:1, 1961.

OETTLE, A. G.: Cancer in Africa, especially in regions south of the Sahara.
J Nat Cancer Inst, 33:383, 1964.

OETTLE, A. G.: The aetiology of primary carcinoma of the liver in Africa:
A critical appraisal of previous ideas with an outline of the mycotoxin
hypothesis. *S Afr Med J, 39*:817, 1965.

OJO, G. O., and PARRATT, J. R.: Urinary excretion of 5-hydroxyindoleacetic
acid in Nigerians with endomyocardial fibrosis. *Lancet, 1*:854, 1966.

OSER, B. L.: Problems related to the use of food additives in the United
States. *Canad Med Ass J, 94*:604, 1966.

OSTWALD, R., and BRIGGS, G. M.: Toxicity of the vitamins; see National
Academy of Sciences, 1966.

PAISSIOS, C. S., and DEMOPOULOS, T.: Human lathyrism. A clinical and
skeletal study. *Clin Orthop, 23*:236, 1962.

PARKE, D. V., and WILLIAMS, R. T.: Liquorice and gastric ulcer. *New
Scientist, 16*:196, 1962.

PATRICK, S. J.; JELLIFFE, D. B., and STUART, K. L.: The hepatic glycogen
content in acute toxic hypoglycaemia. *J Trop Pediat, 1*:88, 1955.

PAUL, O.; LEPPER, M. H.; PHELAN, W. H.; DUPERTUIS, G. W.; MACMILLAN, A.;
McKEAN, H., and PARK, H.: A longitudinal study of coronary heart disease. *Circulation, 28*:20, 1963.

PETERING, H. G.: Foods and feeds as sources of carcinogenic factors. *Nutr
Rev, 24*:321, 1966.

PRESS, E., and YEAGER, L.: Food "poisoning" due to sodium nicotinate.
Amer J Public Health, 52:1720, 1962.

PREUSSMANN, R.; DAIBER, D., and HENGY, H.: A sensitive colour reaction for nitrosamines on thin-layer chromatograms. *Nature, 201*:502, 1964.

PRINZMETAL, M.; SOMMER, H., and LEAKE, C. D. The pharmacological action of "mussel poison." *J Pharm, 46*:63, 1932.

Proceedings of the Third Conference on the Toxicity of Cycads. *Fed Proc, 23*:1337, 1964.

PURCHASE, I. F. H.: Fungal metabolites as potential carcinogens, with particular reference to their role in the aetiology of hepatoma. *S Afr Med J, 41*:406, 1967.

Queries and Minor Notes: Cola drinks. *JAMA, 156*:1376, 1954.

Queries and Minor Notes: Buckwheat poisoning. *JAMA, 159*:1336, 1955.

Questions and Answers: Barbecueing and health hazards. *JAMA, 190*:1019, 1964.

RAMSBOTTOM, J.: *Mushrooms and Toadstools.* London, Collins, 1953.

RAMSBOTTOM, J.: Mushrooms and toadstools. *Proc. Nutr Soc, 12*:39, 1953.

RAO, S. L. N.; SARMA, P. S.; MANKI, K. S., and RAO, T. R. R.: Experimental neurolathyrism in monkeys. *Nature, 214*:610, 1967.

REBER, E. F.; RAHEJA, K., and DAVIS, D.: Wholesomeness of irradiated foods. An annotated bibliography. *Fed Proc, 25*:1529, 1966.

REES, K. R.: Aflatoxin. *Gut, 7*:205, 1966.

REICH, P.; SCHWACHMAR, H., and CRAIN, J. M.: Lycopenemia: A variant of carotenemia. *New Eng J Med, 262*:263, 1960.

REMBOLD, H.: Biologically active substances in royal jelly. *Vitamins Hormones, 23*:359, 1965.

Report: Iodine-131 in milk. *Lancet, 2*:1195, 1961.

Review: Use of sorbitol in medicine. *Nutr Rev, 14*:236, 1956.

Review: Coronary heart disease and dietary habits. *Nutr Rev, 18*:9, 1960.

Review: The laxative effect of dietary roughage. *Nutr Rev, 18*:15, 1960.

Review: Vanadium inhibition of cholesterol synthesis in man. *Nutr Rev, 18*:39, 1960.

Review: Nutritive value of frying oils. *Nutr Rev, 18*:119, 1960.

Review: Hepatic coma. *Nutr Rev, 18*:229, 1960.

Review: Accumulation of insecticides in tissues and excretion in milk. *Nutr Rev, 18*:235, 1960.

Review: Pemmican. *Nutr Rev, 19*:73, 1961.

Review: Toxicity of vitamin K substitutes in premature infants. *Nutr Rev, 19*:75, 1961.

Review: Toxic waterbloom (Algae). *Nutr Rev, 19*:145, 1961.

Review: Strontium-90 in the British diet. *Nutr Rev, 19*:164, 1961.

Review: Food additives. *Nutr Rev, 19*:227, 1961.

Review: Results of treatment in phenylketonuria. *Nutr Rev, 19*:234; 264, 1961.

Review: Dietary components and accumulation of radionuclides in the body. *Nutr Rev, 19*:245, 1961.

Review: Radionuclides, calcium, and potassium in milk. *Nutr Rev, 19*:253, 1961.

Review: Treatment of hypercholesterolemia with nicotinic acid. *Nutr Rev, 19*:325, 1961.

Review: Galactosemia. *Nutr Rev, 20*:43, 1962.

Review: Storage of insecticides in human fats. *Nutr Rev, 20*:52, 1962.

Review: Mechanisms for lowering serum cholesterol concentrations. *Nutr Rev, 20*:72, 1962.

Review: Contaminated peanut meal. *Nutr Rev, 20*:174, 1962.

Review: Mycotoxicoses. — I. Human diseases. *Nutr Rev, 20*:337, 1962.

Review: Mycotoxicoses. — II. Animal diseases. *Nutr Rev, 20*:339, 1962.

Review: Toxic components of lathyrus peas. *Nutr Rev, 21*:28, 1963.

Review: Radionuclides in American diets. *Nutr Rev, 21*:105, 1963.

Review: The celiac syndrome (malabsorption) in pediatrics. *Nutr Rev, 21*: 195, 1963.

Review: Gluten enteropathy. *Nutr Rev, 21*:300, 1963.

Review: Effects of ethanol on plasma lipids in man. *Nutr Rev, 22*:40, 1964.

Review: "Moldy" peanut meal. *Nutr Rev, 22*:49, 1964.

Review: The raw soybean problem in chickens. *Nutr Rev, 22*:58, 1964.

Review: Toxic reactions of vitamin A. *Nutr Rev, 22*:109, 1964.

Review: Reduction of blood lipids by certain compounds. *Nutr Rev, 22*: 134, 1964.

Review: Nicotinic acid and diabetes mellitus. *Nutr Rev, 22*:166, 1964.

Review: Hepatomas in trout. *Nutr Rev, 22*:208, 1964.

Review: Gluten enteropathy: Symptoms versus lesions. *Nutr Rev, 22*:231, 1964.

Review: Attitudes toward fluoridation. *Nutr Rev, 22*:291, 1964.

Review: Hypocholesteremic effect of sitosterol. *Nutr Rev, 22*:326, 1964.

Review: Carbohydrate-induced hypertriglyceridemia. *Nutr Rev, 22*:328. 1964.

Review: Fat and cholesterol in the diet. *Nutr Rev, 23*:3, 1965.

Review: Fatty acid composition of fish oils. *Nutr Rev, 23*:51, 1965.

Review: Dietary carbohydrate and liver lipids. *Nutr Rev, 23*:183, 1965.

Review: Dietary treatment of maple syrup urine disease. *Nutr Rev, 23*:260, 1965.

Review: Vitamin A intoxication in infancy. *Nutr Rev, 23*:263, 1965.

Review: Hydrocarbon residues in cooked and smoked meats. *Nutr Rev, 23*:268, 1965.

Review: Serum phospholipid levels affected by carbohydrate. *Nutr Rev, 23*:292, 1965.

Review: Antibody to milk proteins. *Nutr Rev, 23*:299, 1965.

Review: Cirrhosis in Rhesus monkeys induced by aflatoxin. *Nutr Rev, 23*: 331, 1965.

Review: Acute ethanol intoxication and liver lipid. *Nutr Rev, 23*:338, 1965.

Review: Hepatic steatosis and protein synthesis after alcohol ingestion. *Nutr Rev, 24*:21, 1966.

Review: Blood lipids and various dietary carbohydrates. *Nutr Rev, 24*:35, 1966.

Review: Relationships between alcohol, heart disease, and liver disease. *Nutr Rev, 24*:71, 1966.

Review: Isolation of toxic factors in navy beans. *Nutr Rev, 24*:121, 1966.

Review, The effect of pectin on cholesterol absorption. *Nutr Rev, 24*:209, 1966.

Review: Diet and coronary heart disease. *Nutr Rev, 24*:228, 1966.

Review: Copper toxicity. *Nutr Rev, 24*:305, 1966.

Review: Dietary fat and neoplasms in man. *Nutr Rev, 25*:8, 1967.

Review: Iron — 55 levels in fish and fish-eating populations. *Nutr Rev, 25*: 24, 1967.

Review: Mineral oil in human tissues. *Nutr Rev, 25*:46, 1967.

Review: Effect of dietary protein level on aflatoxin liver injury. *Nutr Rev, 25*:26, 1967.

Review: Dietary intake and fat storage of pesticides. *Nutr Rev, 25*:68, 1967.

Review: Proteolytic activity of raw soybean. *Nutr Rev, 25*:124, 1967.

Review: Diet and heart disease. *Nutr Rev, 25*: 130, 1967.

Review: Atherosclerosis and the hardness of drinking water. *Nutr Rev, 25*: 164, 1967.

REYNOLDS, W. A., and LOWE, F. H.: Mushrooms and a toxic reaction to alcohol. *New Eng J Med, 272*:630, 1965.

RIFKIND, B. M.; LAWSON, D. H., and GALE, M.: Effect of short-term sucrose restriction on serum-lipid levels. *Lancet, 2*:1379, 1966.

ROBINSON, J.; RICHARDSON, A.; CRABTREE, A. N.; COULSON, J. C., and POTTS, G. R.: Organochlorine residues in marine organisms. *Nature, 214*:1307, 1967.

ROBSON, J. M.; SULLIVAN, F. M., and SMITH, R. L.: *Embryopathic Activity of Drugs.* London, Churchill, 1965.

RODAHL, K., and MOORE, T.: The vitamin A content and toxicity of bear and seal liver. *Biochem J, 37*:166, 1943.

ROE, F. J. C., and LANCASTER, M. C.: Natural, metallic and other substances, as carcinogens. *Brit Med Bull, 20*:127, 1964.

RUNDO, J.: Radiocaesium in human beings. *Nature, 188*:703, 1960.

RUSSELL, F. E.: *Marine Toxins and Venomous and Poisonous Marine Animals.* London and New York, Academic, 1965.

RUSSELL, R. S.: *Radioactivity and Human Diet.* Oxford, Pergamon, 1966.

RYAN, C. A., and HUISMAN, O. C.: Chymotrypsin inhibitor 1 from potatoes. *Nature, 214*:1047, 1967.

SAGHIR, A. R.; COWAN, J. W., and SALJI, J. P.: Goitrogenic activity of onion volatiles. *Nature, 211*:87, 1966.

SAKSHAUG, J.; SOGMEN, E.; HANSEN, M. A., and KOPPANG, N.: Dimethylnitrosamine, its hepatotoxic effect in sheep and its occurrence in toxic batches of herring meal. *Nature, 206*: 1261, 1965.

SAPEIKA, N.: Pharmacological actions of plants of the genera Cotyledon and Crassula N.O. Crassulaceae. *Arch Int Pharmacodyn, 44*:307-328, 1936.

SAPEIKA, N.: The excretion of drugs in human milk. *J Obstet Gynaec Brit Emp, 54*:427, 1947.

SAPEIKA, N.: The *Senecio* alkaloids. *S Afr Med J, 26*:485, 1952.

SAPEIKA, N.: Actions of mussel poison. *Arch Int Pharmacodyn, 93*:135, 1953.

SAPEIKA, N.: Mussel poisoning: a recent outbreak. *S Afr Med J, 32*:527, 1958.

SAPEIKA, N. Excretion of drugs, pesticides and radionuclides in milk. *S Afr Med J, 33*:818, 1959.

SAPEIKA, N.; UYS, C. J., and MACKENZIE, D.: The Cape death cup. *S Afr Lab Clin Med, 6*:12, 1960.

SAPEIKA, N., and STEPHENS, E. L.: *Clitocybe toxica*, a new species. *S Afr Med J, 39*:749, 1965.

SAPEIKA, N.: The pharmacology of food. *Practitioner, 194*:661, 1965.

SARGENT, K.; ALLCROFT, R., and CARNAGHAN, R. B. A.: Groundnut toxicity. *Vet Rec, 73*:865, 1961.

SARKAR, S. M.: Isolation from *Argemone* oil of dihydrosanguinarine and sanguinarine: Toxicity of sanguinarine. *Nature, 162*:265, 1948.

SARSIKOV, A. CH.: The problem of the non-medical use of antibiotics. *Antibiotics: Advances in Research, Production and Clinical Use* (Proceedings of the Congress on Antibiotics held in Prague, 1964). London; Butterworths, 1966.

SAYRE, J. W., and KAYMAKCALAN, S.: Cyanide poisoning from apricot seeds among children in central Turkey. *New Eng J Med, 270*:1113, 1964.

SCHANTZ, E. J.: Biochemical studies on paralytic shellfish poisons. *Ann N Y Acad Sci, 90*:843, 1960.

SCHEUER-KARPIN, R.: Poisoning by food plants. *Lancet, 1*:574, 1948.

SCHMID, R.: Cutaneous porphyria in Turkey. *New Eng J Med, 263*:397, 1960.

SCHOENTAL, R.: *Senecio* alkaloids and liver cancer. *Brit Med J, 1*:335, 1954.

SCHOENTAL, R., and MAGEE, P. N.: Further observations on the subacute and chronic liver changes in rats after a single dose of various pyrrolizidine (*Senecio*) alkaloids. *J Path Bact, 78*:471, 1959.

SCHOENTAL, R.: The chemical aspect of Seneciosis. *Proc Roy Soc Med, 53*: 284, 1960.

SCHOENTAL, R.: Liver disease and "natural" hepatotoxins. *Bull WHO, 29*: 823, 1963.

SCHOENTAL, R.: Aflatoxins. *Ann Rev. Pharm, 7*:343, 1967.

SCHOENTAL, R., and BENSTED, J. P. M.: Effects of whole body irradiation and of partial hepatectomy on the liver lesions induced in rats by a single dose of retrorsine, a pyrrolizidine *(Senecio)* alkaloid. *Brit J Cancer,* 17:242, 1963.

SCHOENTAL, R., and WHITE, A. T.: Aflatoxins and "albinism" in plants. *Nature, 205*:57, 1965.

SELLSCHOP, J. P. F.; KRIEK, N. P. J., and DUPREEZ, J. C. G.: Distribution and degree of occurrence of aflatoxin in groundnuts and groundnut products. *S Afr Med J, 39*:771, 1965.

SELZER, G., and PARKER, R. G. F.: Senecio poisoning exhibiting as Chiari's syndrome. *Amer J Path, 27*:885, 1951.

Seventh Report of FAO/WHO Expert Committee on Food Additives. *WHO Techn Rep Ser* No. 281, 1964.

SHULGIN, A. T.: Possible implication of myristicin as a psychotropic substance. *Nature, 210*:380, 1966.

SIMMONDS, N. W.: *Bananas.* London, Longmans, Green, 1960.

SIMON, C.: Nitrite poisoning from spinach. *Lancet, 1*:872, 1966.

SISODIA, C. S., and STOWE, C. M.: The mechanism of drug secretion into bovine milk. *Ann N Y Acad Sci, 111*:650, 1964.

Sixth Report of FAO/WHO Expert Committee on Food Additives. *WHO Techn Rep Ser* No 228, 1962.

SMITH, C. M.: Effects of drugs on the afferent nervous system. In *Drugs Affecting The Peripheral Nervous System.* London, Edward Arnold; New York, Marcel Dekker, 1967, vol. 1, p. 558.

SNIVELEY, W. D.: Discoverer of the cause of milk sickness. *JAMA, 196*:1055, 1966.

STEPHENS, E. L., and KIDD, M. M.: (a) *Some South African Edible Fungi.* (b) *Some South African Poisonous and Inedible Fungi.* 2 volumes. Cape Town, London, New York, Longmans, Green, 1953.

STEYN, D. G.: Poisoning of human beings by weeds contained in cereals (bread poisoning). *Onderstepoort J Vet Sci Anim Ind, 1*:219, 1933.

STEYN, D. G.: Poisoning of animals and human beings by algae. *S Afr J Sci, 41*:243, 1944.

STEYN, D. G.: *Vergiftiging Van Mens en Dier.* Pretoria, South Africa, J. L. van Schaik, 1949.

STEYN, D. G.: Poisoning with the seeds of *Argemone Mexicana* (Mexican Poppy) in human beings. *S Afr Med J, 24*:333, 1950.

STEYN, D. G.: *The Processing of Food and the Contamination of Food and Beverages by Chemicals.* Lantern, 1953-54.

STEYN, D. G.: The problem of methaemoglobinaemia in man with special reference to poisoning with nitrates and nitrites in infants and children. Publication No. 11, Pretoria, University, 1960.

STEYN, D. G.: Grasshopper *(Phymateus leprosus Fabr.)* poisoning in a Bantu child. *S Afr Med J, 36*:822, 1962.

STOB, M.: Estrogens in foods; see National Academy of Sciences, 1966.

STOLL, A., and SEEBECK, E.: Uber Alliin, die genuine Muttersubstanz des Knoblauchols. *Experientia, 3*:114, 1947.

STRAUSS, M. B.: Food Allergens. *Symposium on Foods: Proteins and Their Reactions.* Westport, Conn., Avi Pub, 1964.

STRONG, F. M.: Naturally occurring toxic factors in plants and animals used as food. *Canad Med Ass J, 94*:568, 1966.

STUART, K. L.; JELLIFFE, D. B., and HILL, K. R.: Acute toxic hypoglycaemia occurring in the vomiting sickness of Jamaica. *J Trop Pediat, 1*:69, 1955.

Symposium on additives and residues in human foods. *Amer J Clin Nutr, 9*:259, 1961.

Symposium on mycotoxicosis. A. Human and nutritional aspects; B. Agricultural aspects: *S Afr Med J, 39*:760-778, 1965.

Symposium on toxic factors in foods. *Canad Med Ass J, 94*:567-613, 1966.

Symposium: Nutritional significance of the non-nutrient components of food. *Fed Proc, 25*:102, 1966.

Symposium on toxicity in plastics. *Trans J. Plastics Inst, 35*:447, 1967.

TALBOTT, J. H.: Use of lithium salts as a substitute for sodium chloride. *Arch Intern Med, 85*:1, 1950.

Tea: A Symposium on the Pharmacology and the Physiologic and Psychologic Effects of Tea. Washington 7,, D. C., Biological Sciences Foundation, 1955.

TEELUCKSINGH, D., and SYMONDS, B. E. R.: Hypoglycaemia in rum poisoning. *J Trop Pediat, 7*:119, 1962.

TENNANT, A. D.; NAUBER, J., and CORBEIL, H. E.: An outbreak of paralytic shellfish poisoning. *Canad Med Ass J, 72*:436, 1955.

THATCHER, F. S.: Food-borne bacterial toxins. *Canad Med Ass J, 94*:582, 1966.

THERON, J. J., VAN DER MERWE, K. J.; LIEBENBERG, N.; JOUBERT, H. J. B., and NEL, W.: Acute liver injury in ducklings and rats as a result of ochratoxin poisoning. *J Path Bact, 91*:521, 1966.

THOMAS, J. C. S.: Monoamine-oxidase inhibitors and cheese. *Brit Med J, 2*:1406, 1963.

THOMPSON, M. L.: Carotinaemia in a suckling. *Arch Dis Child, 18*:112, 1943.

Todays Drugs: Agents for lowering serum cholesterol. *Brit Med J, 2*:1181, 1964.

TORSNEY, P. J.: Hypersensitivity to sesame seed. *J Allerg, 35*:514, 1964.

TOWNSEND, G. F.; BROWN, W. H.; FELAUER, E. E., and HAZLETT, B.: Studies on the *in vitro* antitumour activity of fatty acids. *Canad J Biochem Physiol, 39*:1765, 1961.

TRAVERS, P. R.: The results of intoxication with orthocresyl phosphate absorbed from contaminated cooking oil, as seen in 4,029 patients in Morocco. *Proc Roy Soc Med, 55*:57, 1962.

TREASE, G. E.: *A Textbook of Pharmacognosy.* London, Bailliere, Tindall and Cox, 1961.

TULPULE, P. G.; MADHAVEN, T. V., and GOPALAN, C.: Effect of feeding aflatoxin to young monkeys. *Lancet, 1*:962, 1964.

UDENFRIEND, S.; LOVENBERG, W., and SJOERDSMA, A.: Physiologically active amines in common fruits and vegetables. *Arch Biochem Biophys, 85*:487, 1959.

URBACH, E., and GOTTLIEB, P. M.: Allergy. London, William Heinemann, 1946.

UYS, C. J.: National disease patterns in South Africa. *S Afr Med J, 40*:159, 1966.

VAN VEEN, A. G.: Toxic properties of some unusual foods; see National Academy of Sciences, 1966.

VAN WYK, C. P.: Iron absorption and liver iron deposition in the rat. *S Afr Med J, 41*:417, 1967.

VAUGHN, R. H., and STEWART, G. F.: Antibiotics as food preservatives. *JAMA, 174*:1308, 1960.

VINBERG, G. G.: Toxic phytoplankton. Nat. Res. Council, Technical Translation TT-549, Ottawa, 1955.

VINKE, B.: The action of Marmite in nutritional megalobastic anaemia. *Trans Roy Soc Trop Med Hyg, 58*:503, 1964.

WAALKES, T. P.; SJOERDSMA, A.; CREVELING, C. R.; WEISSBACH, H., and UDENFRIEND, S.: Serotonin, norepinephrine, and related compounds in banana. *Science, 127*:648, 1958.

WALKER, A. R. P., and ARVIDSSON, U. B.: Iron "overload" in the South African Bantu. *Trans Roy Soc Trop Med Hyg, 47*:536, 1953.

WALKER, A. R. P.: Nutritional, biochemical and other studies on South African populations. *S Afr Med J, 40*:814, 1966.

WARREN, F. L.: The pyrrolizidine alkaloids. *Fortschr Chem Organ Naturst, 12*:198, 1955.

WARREN, F. L.: The pyrrolizidine alkaloids II. *Fortsch Chem Organ Naturst, 24*:329, 1966.

WATT, J. M., and BREYER-BRANDWYK, M. G.: *The Medicinal and Poisonous Plants of Southern and Eastern Africa,* 2nd ed. Edinburgh and London, Livingstone, 1962.

WEAVER, A. L., and SPITTELL, J. A.: Lathyrism. *Mayo Clin Proc, 39*:485, 1964.

WEIL, A. T.: The use of nutmeg as a psychotropic agent. *Bull Narcot, 18*: 15, 1966.

WEST, G. B.: Tryptamines in edible fruits. *J Pharm Pharmacol, 10*:589, 1958.

WEST, G. B.: Indole derivatives in tomatoes. *J Pharm Pharmacol, 11*:Suppl. 275 T, 1959.

WEST, G. B.:   Carcinoid tumours and pineapples. *J Pharm Pharmacol, 12*: 768, 1960.

WHITING, M. G.:   Food practices in ALS foci in Japan, the Marianas, and New Guinea. *Fed Proc, 23*:1343, 1964.

WIELAND, T., and WIELAND, O.:   Chemistry and toxicology of the toxins of Amanita phalloides. *Pharmacol Rev, 11*:87, 1959.

WIELAND, T.:   Chemical and toxicological studies with cyclopeptides of *Amanita phalloides*. *Pure Appl Chem, 6*:339, 1963.

WILLMOT, F. C., and ROBERTSON, G. W.:   *Senecio* disease. *Lancet, 2*:848, 1920.

WILLS, J. H.:   Goitrogens in foods; see National Academy of Sciences, 1966.

WILLS, J. H.:   Seafood toxins; see National Academy of Sciences, 1966.

WILSON, B. J.:   Fungal toxins; see National Academy of Sciences, 1966.

WILSON, B. J.:   Toxins other than aflatoxins produced by *Aspergillus flavus*. *Bact Rev, 30*:478, 1966.

WILSON, B. J., and WILSON, C. H.:   Toxin from *Aspergillus flavus*: Production on food materials of a substance causing tremors in mice. *Science, 144*:177, 1964.

WOGAN, G. N.:   Chemical nature and biological effects of the aflatoxins. *Bact Rev, 30*:460, 1966.

WOGAN, G. N.:   Physiologically significant food contaminants. *Fed Proc, 25*: 124, 1966.

WOGAN, G. N.:   Current research on toxic food contaminants. *J Amer Diet Ass, 49*:95, 1966.

WOLF, H., and JACKSON, E. W.:   Hepatomas in rainbow trout: Descriptive and experimental epidemiology. *Science, 142*:676, 1963.

WOODWELL, G. M.:   Toxic substances and ecological cycles. *Sci Amer, 216*: 24, 1967.

WRIGHT, R.; TAYLOR, K. B.; TRUELOVE, S. C., and ASCHAFFENBURG, R.: Circulating antibodies to cow's milk proteins and gluten in the newborn. *Brit Med J, 2*:513, 1962.

YANG, M. G.; MICKELSEN, O.; CAMPBELL, M. E.; LAQUEUR, G. L., and KERESZTESY, J. C.:   Cycad flour used by Guamanians: Effects produced in rats by long-term feeding. *J Nutr, 90*:153, 1966.

YUDKIN, J., and MORELAND, J.:   Prevention of ischaemic heart-disease. *Lancet, 2*:1359, 1966.

YUDKIN, J., and RODDY, J.:   Assessment of sugar intake: validity of the questionnaire method. *Brit J Nutr, 20*:807, 1966.

YUDKIN, J.:   Sugar and coronary thrombosis. *New Scientist, 33*:542, 1967.

ZAPP, J. A., and CLAYTON, J. W.:   The pharmacology and toxicology of the environment. *Ann Rev Pharm, 3*:343, 1963.

ZUCKERMAN, A. J., and FULTON, F.:   Acute toxic effects of aflatoxin on human embryo liver cells in culture. *Brit Med J, 2*:90, 1966.

AUTHOR INDEX

Aas, K., 5
Abrams, L., 62
Ahlumalia, H. S., 32
Akinyanju, P., 143
Altman, P. L., 99, 104, 106
Ambrose, A. M., 32, 95
Anderson, W., 90
Antia, F. P., 115
Arena, J. M., 18, 72, 91, 116, 134
Armstrong, D., 66
Arnott, W. M., 29
Arvidsson, U. B., 146
Asano, M., 103
Asatoor, A. M., 93, 94
Ashley, L. M., 62
Asplin, F. D., 62

Baarli, J., 90
Bader, H., 134
Barnes, J. M., 83
Bassett, D. R., 123
Bellet, S., 143
Bergen, S. S., 12
Bewley, T. H., 136
Bingle, J. P., 89
Bird, H. R., 124
Bird, P. M., 90, 132
Bisordi, M. V., 60
Blackwell, B., 48, 93
Block, S. S., 52
Blood, F. R., 28, 42, 55
Bongirwar, D. R., 90
Bonser, G. M., 9, 38
Bothwell, T. H., 146
Boudreaux, H. B., 60
Boyd, W. C., 25
Brandenberger, H., 134
Bras, G., 82
Breyer-Brandwyk, M. G., 16, 18, 20, 21, 22, 23, 27, 28, 30, 32, 35, 39, 45, 50, 59, 64, 71, 78, 80, 138, 148

Briggs, G. M., 12
Brink, A. J., 78
Brock, J. F., 96, 97, 145
Brockington, I. F., 30
Brookes, L. G., 120
Brown, J. M. M., 21, 62
Brown, W. H., 42
Bruce, D. W., 67
Burrell, R. J. W., 53, 147
Butler, W. H., 61, 62, 83

Calvin, M. E., 120
Campbell, G. D., 97, 123, 124
Carnaghan, R. B. A., 62
Carr, W. R., 90
Chapman, R. A., 108, 109
Chen, K. K., 27
Cheung, K. K., 61
Christensen, G. M., 42
Clayton, J. W., 135
Cleave, T. L., 97, 123, 124
Clements, F. W., 92
Clifford, J. I., 62
Coady, A., 69
Colhoun, E. H., 42
Comar, C. L., 90, 95, 132, 135
Crawford, M. A., 30
Crosby, D. G., 68
Crout, J. R., 29
Culvenor, C. C. J., 83

Dahl, L. K., 120
Davidson, S., 23, 85, 97
Day, P. L., 109
Dayan, A. D., 42
Dean, G., 76
Deichmann, W. B., 28, 40
de Jong, J. C., 92
De Matteis, F., 76
Demopoulos, T., 64
De Recondo, A. M., 63

169

Dewberry, E. B., 18, 41, 42, 50, 99, 127, 139
de Wet, P. J., 21
de Wit, J. P., 9, 61
Dickens, F., 61, 62
Diener, U. L., 62
Dittmer, D. S., 99, 104, 106
Dixit, P. K., 43
Doll, R., 89
Dreisbach, R. H., 99
Drill, V., 97, 122, 142
Dugan, S., 136
Duguid, J. B., 32
Dunachie, J. F., 95
Dungal, N., 133
Dybing, O., 83

Eagle, E., 57
Earle, K. V., 45
Egan, H., 90
Elkington, S. G., 63
Elliot, W., 52
Erichsen, S., 83
Evans, M. H., 102

Fänge, R., 103
Fassett, D. W., 22, 23, 137
Feigen, G. A., 103
Felauer, E. E., 42
Feng, P. C., 27
Feuell, A. J., 9, 69, 76, 129
Finberg, L., 120
Fingerman, M., 102
Fisher, H., 41
Fistein, B., 27
Fitzhugh, O. G., 9
Fletcher, W. W., 95
Forgacs, J., 129
Foy, H., 61, 83
Foy, J. M., 29, 67
Frampton, V., 60
Frost, D. V., 21
Fuhrman, F. A., 105
Fulton, F., 63

Gabbai, 78
Garrod, L. P., 130
George, E., 140
Gerarde, H. W., 28, 40
Gilman, A., 12, 13, 97, 137
Gleason, M. N., 42, 116, 131
Godfrey, C. M., 58
Goldblith, S. A., 119
Goodman, L. S., 12, 13, 97, 137
Gosselin, R. E., 131
Gottlieb, P. M., 4, 5
Green, R. C., 55
Green, R. G., 139
Greer, M. A., 24, 32, 33
Gross, E. G., 44
Gyorgy, L., 67

Halbert, E., 66
Hall, R. L., 115
Halstead, B. W., 88, 99, 100, 101, 102
Haneveld, G. T., 104
Hannington, E., 5, 94
Harding, J. D. J., 60
Harington, J. S., 64
Harman, D., 96
Havre, G. N., 106
Hawk, P. B., 87
Heiner, D. C., 92
Hickman, R., 146
Hill, K. R., 61, 82
Hodge, H. C., 131
Hodge, J. V., 31
Hodges, R. E., 131
Holliday, M. A., 136
Holzapfel, C. W., 61
Hoong, Loo, Y., 11
Horvath, I., 121
Horwitz, D., 93, 145
Hsia, D. Y., 11
Hudson, T. G. F., 97
Hueper, W. C., 7, 109, 114, 117, 129, 133
Huisman, F., 73
Huisman, O. C., 68
Hvinden, T., 90

Isaacson, C., 146
Itoh, M., 103

Jackson, E. W., 57
Jankelson, O. M., 143
Jelliffe, D. B., 48, 64, 115
Jones, W. O., 46, 62

Kao, C. Y., 100, 101, 102, 105
Kaymakcalan, S., 28
Kean, E. A., 27
Keele, C. A., 66
Keidan, S. E., 60
Keiser, H. R., 65
Kekwick, A., 8
Kellaway, C. H., 102
Kidd, M. M., 49, 50
Kingsbury, J. M., 18
Knotek, Z., 93
Knowles, J. A., 90
Kraybill, H. F., 7, 61, 116, 119, 126, 133
Kumta, U. S., 90
Kun, E., 121
Kuo, P. T., 123

Lancaster, M. C., 9, 71, 129, 146
Laqueur, G. L., 37
Lea, C. H., 112
Leake, C. D., 70, 144
Legator, M., 63
Lennard-Jones, J. E., 89
Lepkovsky, S., 13, 48
Levene, C. I., 65
Liener, I. E., 20, 25, 31, 32, 65, 66
Lijinsky, W., 61
Lillegraven, A., 90
List, P. H., 54
Little, J. A., 123, 143
Locket, S., 12, 18, 25, 28, 41, 42, 44, 89, 91, 93, 137, 139
Loosmore, R. M., 60
Lowe, F. H., 54

Mabbitt, L. A., 48, 93
Macdonald, I., 123
Mackenzie, D., 50
Madshus, K., 90
Magee, P. N., 38, 82
Mainwaring, D., 60
Mann, T. P., 93
Mansmann, H. C., 4, 75, 92, 94
Manson-Bahr, P. H., 25, 44, 45
Marko, P., 43
Marley, E., 48
Marshall, P. B., 29
McGlashan, N. D., 147
McNeill, K. G., 90
Meneely, G. R., 120
Mercer, E. R., 90
Meyer, K. F., 99
Meyler, L., 12, 44, 90, 97
Mickelson, O., 32, 37, 57, 106
Miller, D. S., 90
Miller, E. C., 38, 129, 146
Miller, J. A., 9, 38, 129, 146
Moffie, D., 104
Molhusen, J. A., 44
Molnar, G. D., 13, 97
Molnar, J., 67
Montgomery, R. S., 20, 31, 47, 64
Moore, T., 87
Morrison, A. B., 108, 109
Mosher, H. S., 105
Murphy, K. J., 116
Murtha, E. F., 101, 102

Neame, P. B., 63
Nicholls, L., 47, 48, 64, 78, 115
Nieman, C., 44
Novellie, L., 146
Nuessle, W. F., 107

O'Donovan, M. B., 146
Oettle, A. G., 63, 83, 147
Ojo, G. O., 29
Oser, B. L., 109
Ostwald, R., 12

Paissios, L. S., 64
Parke, D. V., 44
Parker, R. G. F., 63, 82
Parratt, J. R., 29, 67
Passmore, R., 23, 85, 97
Patel, N. G., 43
Patrick, S. J., 25
Paul, O., 143
Petering, H. G., 9, 38
Pillay, V. K. G., 63
Press, E., 86
Preussman, R., 53
Prinzmetal, M., 102
Purchase, I. F. H., 9, 63, 70

Ramsbottom, J., 49
Rao, S. L. N., 65
Reber, E. F., 119
Rees, K. R., 62
Reich, P., 72
Reith, H., 54
Rembold, H., 43
Reynolds, W. A., 54
Rifkind, B. M., 123
Ritman, P., 11
Robertson, G. W., 82
Robinson, J., 8, 131
Robson, J. M., 90
Rodahl, K., 87
Roddy, J., 123
Roe, F. J. C., 9, 71, 129, 146
Roels, O. A., 12
Rudolph, G. G., 28, 42, 55
Russell, F. E., 99, 100, 102
Russell, R. S., 132
Ryan, C. A., 68

Saghir, A. R., 34, 59
Sakshaug, J., 107, 119
Sapeika, N., 15, 50, 52, 80, 86, 90, 100, 101, 102, 104
Sargeant, K., 60
Sarkar, S. M., 78
Sarsikov, A. Ch., 42, 124
Sayre, J. W., 28

Schantz, E. J., 102
Scheuer-Karpin, R., 29
Schmid, R., 76
Schmidt, P., 93
Schoental, R., 9, 38, 61, 63, 80, 82, 83
Seebeck, E., 39
Selzer, G., 63, 82
Shulgin, A. T., 55
Silverman, M., 70, 144
Sim, G. A., 61
Simmonds, N. W., 30
Simon, C., 22
Sinclair, H. M., 48, 64, 115
Sisodia, C. S., 90
Sjoerdsma, A., 29, 65
Smith, C. M., 66
Smith, M. V., 42
Sniveley, W. D., 91
Spittell, J. A., 65
Stephens, E. L., 49, 50
Stewart, G. F., 112
Steyn, D. G., 16, 18, 22, 42, 75, 78, 80, 85, 93, 137
Stoll, A., 39
Stob, M., 22, 32
Stowe, C. M., 90
Strauss, M. B., 4
Strong, F. M., 19, 36, 37, 66
Stuart, K. L., 25
Symonds, B. E. R., 27

Talbott, J. H., 120
Teelucksingh, D., 27
Thatcher, F. S., 4
Theron, J. J., 62
Thomas, J. C. S., 93
Thomson, M. L., 34
Torsney, P. J., 58
Townsend, G. F., 43
Travers, P. R., 58
Trease, G. E., 66, 71
Trojan, O. A. D., 90
Tulpule, P. G., 61

Udenfriend, S., 19, 29
Urbach, E., 4, 5
Uys, C. J., 50, 146

van Veen, A. G., 25, 44, 72
van Wyk, C. P., 146
Vasbinder, H., 73
Vaughn, R. H., 112
Vinberg, G. G., 138
Vinke, B., 48

Waalkes, T. P., 29
Walker, A. R. P., 146
Warren, F. L., 80
Watt, J. M., 16, 18, 20, 21, 22, 23, 27, 28, 30, 32, 35, 39, 45, 50, 59, 64, 71, 78, 138, 148
Weaver, A. L., 65, 80
Weedon, D. G., 66
Weil, A. T., 55
West, G. B., 67, 72

White, A. J., 63
Whitehair, L. A., 119, 126
Whiting, M. G., 37
Wieland, D., 50
Wieland, T., 50
Wigglesworth, J. S., 62
Williams, R. T., 44
Willmot, F. C., 82
Wills, J. H., 24, 34, 99, 104
Wilson, B. J., 9, 61, 63, 69, 70, 79, 129
Wilson, C. H., 63
Wogan, G. N., 9, 61, 62, 63, 127
Wolf, H., 57
Woodwell, G. M., 8, 90, 130, 132
Wright, R., 75, 92

Yang, M. G., 32, 37, 57, 106
Yeager, L., 86
Yudkin, L., 123, 143

Zapp, J. A., 135
Zuckerman, A. J., 63

SUBJECT INDEX

A

Abalone, 103
Acacia, 20, 40
Acacipetalin, 20
Acetylacetate, 116
Ackee, 25
Acorns, 55, 143
Acrinyl isothiocyanate, 54
Active principles in plants, 18
Acute alimentary myositis, 138
Additives, 5, 110
Adenia, 17
Adrenaline, 18
Aflatoxins, 9, 38, 60, 129
Agar, 40, 71
Agave americana, 148
Agglutinins, 25
Aglycones, 38
Alcohol, 135, 144
Aldrin, 131
Aleukia, 76
Aleurites fordii, 73
Algae, 40, 138
Alginic acid, 70
Alimentary toxic aleukia, 76
Alkali disease, 21, 72, 91
Alkaloids, 51, 66, 67, 73, 78, 79
Alkylating agents, 83
Allergy, 4, 10, 99, 103
Allicin, 39
Alliin, 39
Allium cepa, 58
Allium sativum, 39
Allspice, 115
Allylisothiocyanate, 54
Allyl propyl disulphide, 39
Allylthiocarbamide, 43
Almond, 23, 27
Amanita, 50
Amanitins, 27, 50
Amaranth, 113
Amines, 18

Amygdalin, 27, 46
Anemia, 30, 48, 106
Anemones, 102
Animal feeds, 124
Anise, 41
Antabuse, 54
Antacid, 89
Anthraquinone, 68, 70
Antibiotics, 8, 90, 111, 130
Antibodies, 92
Anticholinesterase, 68
Antidepressants, 85, 93
Anti-sprouting agents, 68
Anti-staling agents, 75
Antithiamine, 138
Antithyroid principles, 24
Antitrypsin, 31
Antivitamins, 95, 138
Antoxidants, 110, 112
Apiol, 58
Apples, 20, 27
Apricots, 20, 28
Arabin, 40
Arachidonic acid, 95
Arachis oil, 57
Argemone mexicana, 77
Armoracia, 43
Arrack, 70, 148
Arsenic, 139
Artichoke, 41
Arylalkylamines, 19
Asparagus, 28
Aspergilli, 9, 60
Aspergillus flavus, 60
Asthma, 5, 94
Atherosclerosis, 32, 41, 95, 136
Atriplicism, 28
Atromid-S, 96
Avidin, 95
Avocado, 19
Azaleas, 42

174

B

Bacon, 118
Bacterial poisoning, 4
Balloon fishes, 104
Bamboo shoots, 20, 28
Bananas, 19, 29, 112
Bantu beer, 20, 146
Barracudas, 104
Bass, 104
Beans, 23, 25, 30
Beer
  banana, 30
  Bantu, 20
  honey, 43
  rice, 70
  root, 116, 145
Beet, sugar, 123
Beetroot, 23
Beets, 22
Benzoic acid, 118
Benzpyrene, 129, 133
Benzyl cyanide, 36
Benzylisothiocyanate, 36
Beta-aminopropionitrile, 65
Betel nut, 32
Beverages, 135
Bezoars, 40
Biogastrone, 44
Birds, 8
Blaasops, 104
Bleaching agents, 110
Blind staggers, 21, 72
Blighia sapida, 25
Blow-fishes, 104
Bonitos, 105
Borax, 119
Bore-hole water, 93, 137
Boric acid, 93, 119
Botulism, 4
Bovine hyperkeratosis, 127
Bovril, 84, 88, 94
Bran, 74
Brassicae, 24, 32
Brasso, 147
Bread, 75, 110, 111
Bread additives, 110
Bread mould, 75

Bread poisoning, 75
Bream, 138
Broad bean, 30, 94
Broccoli, 22, 68
Broiled meat, 133
Bromelain, 24, 67
Brussel sprouts, 33
Bubble gum, 40
Buckwheat, 32
Budd-Chiari syndrome, 63
Burma bean, 31
Burnett's syndrome, 89
Bush-tea, 63, 82, 142
Butterpit, 17
Butyl-hydroxyanisole, 110, 112
Butylphthalate, 134

C

Cabbage, 22, 32
Cesium, 132
Caffeine, 135, 139
Calcium, 23, 69
Calcium carbimide, 54
Cantharidin, 147
Capsaicin, 66
Capsicum, 66
Carbenoxalone, 44
Carcinogens, 7, 9, 86, 96, 133
Carcinoid, 29
Cardiomyopathy, 145
Caribou, 132
Carica papaya, 24
Caries, 123
Carminatives, 115, 142
Carotenaemia, 34, 45
Carotene, 34
Carotenoderma, 34
Carotenoids, 35
Carp, 139
Carrageenin, 71
Carrageen moss, 70
Carrots, 34
Casein, 11
Cashew nut, 23, 35
Cassava, 46
Castor bean, 25, 30
Cataracts, 11

Cauliflower, 22
Cayenne pepper, 66
Celiac disease, 10, 75
Chavicine, 66
Cheese, 18, 88, 93
Chenopodium, 29
Cherries, 20, 111, 117
Chianti, 94, 136, 145
Chiari syndrome, 63, 82
Chick hydropericardium, 127
Chick pea, 143
Chicken liver, 94
Chicory, 143
Chillies, 66
Chinese-wood oil, 73
Chlorinated hydro carbons, 130
Chlorine dioxide, 75
Chlorogenic acid, 142
Chlorophenothane, 130
Chocolate, 144
Cholesterol, 95, 96, 98
Cholinesterase, 68
Cichorium intybus, 143
Cicutoxin, 42
Cidivici, 53, 146
Ciguatera, 104
Cirrhosis, 10, 61, 69, 85, 145
Citric acid, 110
Citrinin, 70
Clams, 99, 100
Classification of foods, 13, 14
Claviceps purpurea, 77
Clitocybe, 52
Clofibrate, 96
Clover, 35
Cobalamins, 87
Coca-Cola, 139
Cocoa, 23, 140, 144
Coco de mono, 28
Cod-liver oil, 107
Coeliac disease (*see* Celiac disease)
Coffee, 23, 134, 140, 142
Cola, 139
Colostrum, 92
Coloring agents, 110, 113
Condiments, 115
Coniine, 41
Conium maculatum, 41

Constipation, 123
Contaminants, 5, 106, 127
Cooking oil, 58
Cool drinks, 139
Copper, 125, 139
Coprinus, 54
Coronary heart disease, 123
Cottonseed meal, 57
Cottonseed oil, 57, 95
Cotyledonosis, 86
Crab, 85, 103
Crab meat, 85
Crawfish, 100
Cress, 36, 54
Crustaceans, 103
Cucurbitaceae, 17, 49
Cucurbitacins, 17
Cumin, 115
Currants, 23
Cyano-alanine, 65
Cyanocobalamins, 87
Cyanogens, 19
Cycads, 37
Cycloalliin, 59
Cycasin, 37
Cyclamates, 121
Cyclopeptides, 50, 70
Cytosiderosis, 146

D

Daidzein, 32
Dates, 17
Datura, 42, 77
DDT, 8, 130
Death cup, 49
Depilatory, 72
Diabetes mellitus, 97, 123
Diallyldisulphide, 39
Diaminobutyric acid, 65
Diarrhoea, 56
Dicophane, 130
Dicoumarol, 35
Dieldrin, 131, 134
Dihydroxyphenylalanine, 31
Dimethylnitrosamine, 38, 107
Dinoflagellates, 100

Dioscorea, 73
Dioscorine, 73
Diosgenin, 73
Disulfiram, 54
Djenkol beans, 43
Dopa, 31
Dopamine, 18, 31
Drinks, 135
Dropwort, 42
Ducklings, 60
Dyes, 113

E

Eels, 138
Eggplant, 19, 68
Eggs, 35, 94
Elephant's foot, 74
Emulsin, 27
Encephalartos, 17
Endemic goitre, 137
Endomyocardial fibrosis, 29
Enzootic icterus, 21
Enzymes, 24, 67, 72
Epicladosporic acid, 76
Epidemic dropsy, 78
Ergot, 78
Ergotamine, 79
Ergotism, 78
Erythromelalgia, 29
Erythrosine, 117
Eskimo, 132
Esophageal cancer, 53, 64, 146
Essential oils, 115
Estrogens, 22, 125
Euphorbone, 45

F

Faddists, 12
Fagicladosporic acid, 76
Fagopyrism, 32
FAO/WHO, 113
Fat Hen, 29
Fats, 56, 98
Fatty acids, 57, 96, 145
Fava bean, 11, 30
Favism, 11
Feeding-formulae, 92

Feeds, animal, 124
Fermented drinks, 148
Ficus carica, 38
Ficusin, 39
Figs, 38
Fish-liver oils, 107
Flavoring agents, 110, 115
Flax, 57
Flour, 37, 74
Fluorides, 127, 135, 136
Food
    additives, 5, 108
    allergy, 4
    antibiotics in, 111, 130
    bacterial poisoning, 4
    carcinogens, 7
    classification, 13
    contaminants, 5, 106, 127
    definition, 3
    faddists, 12
    general considerations, 3
    mycotoxins in, 129
    pesticides in, 130
    preservation, 118
    processing, 132
Food additives
    classification, 110
    definition, 108
    types, 110
Food Additives and Contaminants
    Committee, 6, 121
Foods and Drugs Act (Canada), 108
Food and Drug Administration, 6, 116
Food containers, 134
Food, Drug and Cosmetic Act, 6, 113
Foods, Drugs and Disinfectants
    Act, 82, 113
Food Standards Committee, 113, 114
Foodstuff, 3
Fowls, 21
Foxes, 138
Fox liver, 87
Fraxin, 47
Fruits, 16
Fruits, fermented, 148
Fruit juices, 135, 139
Fucoidin, 71
Fugu poison, 105

Fungi, 9, 49
Fungicides, 130
Furo-coumarin, 38
Fusariogenin, 76
Fusarium, 76
Fusel oil, 146

G

Galactosaemia, 11
Gangrene, 79
Garlic, 39, 54
Gastric ulcer, 44
Gastropods, 103
Geeldikkop, 21
Gelidium, 71
Genistein, 32
Genistin, 32
Ginger paralysis, 58
Glaucoma, 122
Gliadin, 74
Globe fishes, 104
Glucobrassicin, 33
Gluconasturtin, 36
Glucose -6- phosphate dehydrogenase, 11, 31
Glutamates, 120
Glutamic acid, 116, 120
Glutelin, 74
Gluten, 5, 10, 74
Glycerin, 122
Glycosides, 19, 36, 37, 46, 54
Glycyrrhetinic acid, 44
Glycyrrhiza, 44
Goatfish, 106
Goitrin, 33
Goitrogens, 24, 32, 92, 137
Goldenrod, rayless, 91
Gossypol, 57
Grain, 79
Granadilla, 17
Grasshoppers, 18
Ground nuts, 57
Ground nut oil, 57
Guarana, 143
Gums, 40
Gymnothorax, 104

H

Haff disease, 138
Halibut-liver oil, 88, 107
Ham, 118
Heart disease, 123
Hemagglutinin, 32
Hematinics, 87
Hemlock, 41
Hemophilia, 60
Hepatomas, 57, 63, 69, 116
Hepatotoxins, 21, 38, 61, 70
Herbal teas, 142
Herring, 88, 94
Herring meal, 107
Herring, pickled, 107
Hexachlorobenzene, 76
Hexoestrol, 125
Hobbs, Anna Pierce, 91
Honey, 42
Horse bean, 30
Horseradish, 43, 54
Humectants, 111
Hydrocarbons, 86, 117, 130, 133
Hydrocyanic acid, 20
Hydroxocobalamin, 87
Hydroxybenzoate, 118
Hydroxymethyl indole, 33
Hydroxytryptamine, 18, 29, 67, 72
Hyperbilirubinaemia, 11
Hypercalcaemia, 12, 89
Hypercarotenosis, 12, 34
Hypercholesterolaemia, 97
Hypersensitivity, 5, 38
Hypervitaminosis, 12, 87
Hypoglycaemia, 25
Hypoglycins, 26
Hypokalaemia, 23
Hypovitaminosis, 13

I

Iceland, 133
Ichthyosarcotoxism, 104
Icterus, 21
Inborn errors of metabolism, 11
Indole acetonitrile, 33
Inky cap, 54, 135
Inocybe, 51

Insecticides, 8, 130
Intoxicating beverages, 144
Iodine, 71, 117, 137
Ionizing radiation, 119
Irish moss, 71
Iron, 106, 145, 146
Isin, 25
Islanditoxin, 70

J

Jack bean, 25
Jacks, 104
Jake paralysis, 58
Jamaica ginger, 58
Jams, 41
Java bean, 31
Jellies, 41, 71
Jengcolic acid, 43
Jenghol seed, 43
Jerusalem artichoke, 41
Jesuit tea, 144
Jetberry bush, 27
Jimmy weed, 91

K

Kaffir, bread, 17
Kaffir corn, 19, 20, 146
Kaffir orange, 16
Kale, 32
Karaya gum, 40
Kelps, 71
Kernicterus, 13
Knoblauch, 39
Koji, 70
Kola, 143
Krimpsiekte, 86
Kwashiorkor, 88

L

Laminarin, 71
Lathyrism, 64
Lathyrus species, 64
Lead, 137
Lecithin, 94
Lectins, 25

Legumes, 25
Lemon juice, 139
Lepidium, 36
Lettuce, 22
Leucaena glauca, 72
Lichens, 132
Licorice, 44
Lima beans, 20, 31
Lincoln family, 91
Lindane, 130
Linoleic acid, 95
Linolenic acid, 95
Linseed, 57
Linseed oil, 57, 95
Lipids, 95, 123
Lipoproteins, 96
Liquid paraffin, 117
Liquid petrolatum, 117
Liquorice, 44
Lithium, 120
Liver, 12, 87
Lobsters, 100, 104
Locusts, 18
Lucerne, 35
Luteoskyrin, 70
Lycopenes, 72

M

Mace, 55, 116
Mackerel, 104
Macrozamin, 37
Maize, 19, 45
Malovu, 148
Manchineel, 45
Mangiferin, 45
Mangoes, 34, 45
Manihot, 46
Manioc, 20, 46
Manna, 47, 122
Mannitol, 47, 71, 122
MAOI, 85, 93
Maple syrup urine disease, 11
Marfan's syndrome, 64
Marine animals, 99
Marmite, 48, 94
Marrows, 17, 49
Marula, 148

Maté, 114
Mead, 43
Mealie, 45
Meat, 84, 133
Meat extracts, 84
Melons, 49, 111
Metal poisoning, 139
Metals, 21
Methemoglobinaemia, 22, 93, 137
Methyl alcohol, 140
Methylazoxymethanol, 37
Methylcellulose, 117
Methylthiouracil, 125
Mexican poppy, 78
Microorganisms, 4
Migraine, 5, 94
Milk, 88
Milk sickness, 91
Millet, 19, 20, 146
Mimosa, 20
Mimosine, 72
Mineral oil, 117
Ministry of Agriculture, Fisheries,
    and Food, 109
Mink, 106
Molds, 60, 69, 75, 94
Molluscs, 99
Molybdenum, 53
Monoamine oxidase, 85, 88, 93, 107
Mottled teeth, 136
Mucilages, 40
Mullet, 106
Muscarine, 51
Mushrooms, 49
Mussels, 99
Mustard, 24, 33, 54
Mustard oil, 54
Myceto-atropine, 51
Mycotoxins, 38, 61, 129
Myoglobinuria, 44
Myristicin, 42, 55
Myrosin, 54

N

Naphthalenes, 127
Nasturtium, 36
Navy beans, 32

Neptuna, 103
Nerium oleander, 18, 42, 86, 91, 138
Neuritis, 58
Neurolathyrism, 64, 65
Neurotoxic substances, 105, 127
Newts, 105
Nicotinic acid, 13, 86, 97
Nisin, 111
Nitrates, 22, 85, 93, 118, 137
Nitriles, 19, 64, 65
Nitrites, 85, 93, 118, 137
Nitrosamines, 9, 53
Noradrenaline, 18
Nutmeg, 55, 116
Nutriment, 3
Nystatin, 112

O

Oak, 55
Ochratoxin, 62
Odoratism, 64
Oenanthotoxin, 42
Oesophageal cancer (*see* Esophageal)
Oestrogens (*see* Estrogens)
Oils, 56
Oils, essential, 115
Oleic acid, 95
Oligophrenia, 11
Onions, 34, 54, 58
Opuntia, 148
Orache, 29
Orange, 16, 19
Organo-chlorine residues, 8
Orthocresylphosphate, 58
Osteolathyrism, 64
Oxalates, 22, 69
Oxalic acid, 23
Oxazolidones, 34
Oxo, 84
Oxyphenisatin, 68

P

Palm trees, 148
Pancreatitis, 145
Papain, 24

Papayas, 24, 34
Paprika, 67
Paraguay tea, 144
Paralytic shellfish toxin, 100
Parsley, 41, 42
Parsnips, 41
Passion fruit, 17
Pawpaw, 24
Peanut oil, 57
Peanuts, 59
Peas, 64
Pectins, 40
Pemmican, 85
Penicillium islandicum, 61, 69
Pepper, 66
Pepsi-Cola, 139
Perch, 104, 138
Pesticides, 8, 90, 130
Pheochromocytoma, 29
Phalloidins, 27, 50
Phaseolunatin, 31, 46
Phasiolus, 31
Phenylalanine, 11
Phenylketonuria, 11
Photosensitization, 29, 38, 103
Phytoagglutinins, 25
Phytoplankton, 138
Phytoserin, 55
Pigs, 60, 124
Pimento, 115
Pineapples, 19, 67
Piper, 66
Plankton, 138
Plantago seed, 40
Plantain, 19, 23, 29
Plants, as foods, 16
Plastic containers, 134
Plums, 17, 19, 20
Poisonous fruits, 16
Polar bear liver, 12, 87, 107
Polysaccharides, 40, 70, 74
Ponceau, 114
Poppy weed, 78
Porphyria, 12, 76, 146
Potassium, 23
Potassium iodate, 75
Potassium oxalate, 22
Potato, 19, 67

Poultry, 111, 124
Preservatives, 110, 118
Pricklypear, 17
Primaquine, 11
Processing, 132
Propenyl sulfenic acid, 59
Propylacetate, 116
Proteins, 25, 84
Proteolytic enzymes, 31, 38, 67
Prunasin, 27
Prunes, 20, 23, 68
Psillium seed, 40
Psilocybe, 52
Puffers, 104
Pulque, 148
Pyorrhoea, 123
Pyrrolizidines, 82

Q

Quercus, 55

R

Radionuclides, 10, 90, 131
Radish, 54
Rangoon bean, 31
Rape, 22, 33
Raynaud's disease, 29
Red water, 100
Reindeer, 132
Rhododendrons, 42
Rhubarb, 23, 68
Rice, 69
Rice beer, 70
Rice wine, 70
Ricin, 30
Ricinus, 77
Robin, 18
Rodenticides, 130
Roe, 106
Rooibostee, 142
Royal jelly, 42
Russula, 50
Rutabaga, 22, 24
Rye, 78

S

Saccharin, 121
Saccharine disease, 123
Safrole, 116, 145
Sago, 17
Sake, 70
Salads, 36
Salmon, 107
Salt, 119
Salt substitutes, 120
Sanguinarine, 78
Sarsaparilla, 116
Sassafras, 116
Sauce, 115
Sauerkraut, 139
Saury, 106
Sausages, 133
Saxitoxin, 99
Scallops, 99, 111
Sea cucumbers, 103
Seafood, 99
Sea urchins, 103
Seal liver, 87, 107
Seaweed, 70
Seeds, 25
Selenium, 21, 72
Senecio, 63, 77, 80
Serotonin, 18
Sesame oil, 58
Sesamin, 58
Shark liver, 87, 105
Shellfish, 99
Shrimps, 111
Sinalbin, 54
Sinigrin, 43, 54
Sitosterols, 96
Slugs, 103
Snails, 103
Snake-root, 91
Snapper, 104
Sodium benzoate, 118
Sodium cyclamate, 121
Sodium dimethyl dithiocarbamate, 111
Sodium nicotinate, 86
Sodium propionate, 111
Soft drinks, 135, 139
Solanine, 67, 72
Sorbic acid, 111, 118

Sorbitol, 122
Sorghum, 20, 146
Sorrel, 23
Soybean, 22, 24, 31
Specific dynamic effect, 84
Spices, 115
Spinach, 22, 23, 69
Sponges, 102
Springkaanbos, 82
Sprue, 75
Squashes, 17, 34, 49
St. Anthony's fire, 79
Starfishes, 102
Steaks, 86
Sterculia, 40
Sterigmatocystin, 61
Sterols, 96
Stilboestrol, 125
Stilton cheese, 93
Strawberries, 71, 111
Strontium-90, 132
Strychnos species, 16
Sucaryl, 121
Sucrose, 122
Sugar, 122
Sugar beet, 123
Sulphoraphane, 36
Sulphur dioxide, 118
Sunset yellow, 114
Surgeon fish, 104
Surra, 148
Swedes, 22, 33
Sweetening agents, 120
Sweet potato, 34
Sweets, 116
Synthalin, 27

T

Tabasco pepper, 66
Tamarind, 72
Tamarisk, 47
Tannin, 140
Tapioca, 46
Tares, 64
Tarichotoxin, 105
Tartrazine, 5, 114
Tea, 23, 82, 140

Temba, 148
Tetracyclines, 119
Tetramine, 103
Tetrodotoxin, 103, 105
Theobromine, 140, 144
Theophylline, 140
Thiamine, 138
Thiocyanate, 33
Thioglucoside, 33
Thiooxazolidones, 24, 33
Thyroxine, 96
Toadfishes, 104
Toadstools, 49
Tobacco, 44
Toddy, 148
Tomato, 19, 72
Tooth enamel, 135
Toxins, bacterial, 4
Toyon, 27
Tragacanth, 40
Tranylcypromine, 48
Traveller's diarrhoea, 56
Trembles, 91
Tremetol, 92
Triglycerides, 56, 123, 145
Triorthocresylphosphate, 58
Trout, 57
Trypsin inhibitor, 24, 31
Tryptamine, 72
Tunas, 105, 107
Tung oil, 73
Tung nuts, 73
Turkeys, 60
Turnips, 22, 24, 33
Turtle, 106
Typhoid, 99
Tyramine, 5, 18, 48, 85, 93

U

Ukanya, 148
Ulcers, 44, 89, 123
Unsaturated fatty acids, 96
Urticaria, 5, 94
Ustilago, 45

V

Vanadium, 97

Veno-occlusive disease, 63, 82, 142
Vetches, 64
Vicia fava, 30
Vitamin A, 12, 34, 87, 88
Vitamin B, 48
Vitamin D, 12
Vitamin K, 11, 13
Vomiting sickness, 25

W

Water, 135
Watercress, 36
Watermelons, 17
Weed-killers, 130
Well-water, 93, 137
Whale liver, 87, 107
Wheat, 74
Whelks, 103
WHO Expert Committee, 109, 114
WHO/FAO, 8, 109
Wild date, 17
Wild lime, 148
Wild orange, 16
Wild plum, 148
Wild tomato, 72
Wine, 94
  honey, 43
  palm, 148
  rice, 70

X

Xanthines, 140
Ximenia, 148

Y

Yams, 73
Yeast, 48
Yellow rice, 69
Yellowsis, 69
Yerba, 144
Yogurt, 88
Yolk, 35, 94

Z

Zea mays, 45
Zinc, 132, 139, 147